Candy Coated
CHUNK OF GRANITE

The Inspiring Journey of One Woman's
Valiant Battle with Metastatic Breast Cancer

by Cindy Welsh Colangelo
with Joe Colangelo and Ellen Welsh Elam

Inspire On Purpose Publishing
Irving, Texas

Candy-Coated Chunk of Granite:

The Inspiring Journey of One Woman's
Valiant Battle with Metastatic Breast Cancer

Copyright © 2015 Joseph Colangelo

Inspire on Purpose Publishing
Irving, Texas
(888) 403-2727
http://inspireonpurpose.com
The Platform Publisher™

Printed in the United States of America

Library of Congress Control Number: 2015942260

ISBN-13: 978-1-941782-18-7

Dedication

To all the patients burdened with the weight
of a cancer diagnosis ...

To all the family members and friends
who love and care for them ...

To all the doctors, nurses, lab techs, and other support
staff who somehow manage to change bandages, hold
hands, and keep families together while everything else
is falling apart ...

You are our inspiration for sharing this journey.

To you we dedicate Cindy Colangelo's
beautiful words, stories, and life-changing
moments of affirmation.

CC, our beautiful mother, wife, sister, aunt, daughter,
and friend, will live forever in our hearts.

Acknowledgments

In addition to drawing inspiration and comfort from books such as *Jesus Calling* by Sarah Young and *Just Enough Light for the Step I'm On* by Stormie Omartian, Cindy was also supported by many great organizations and their dedicated volunteers. Her family would like to thank the following organizations and offer them as resources for cancer patients and their families:

- Susan G. Komen — www.komen.org

- CaringBridge — www.caringbridge.org

- Faith Presbyterian Hospice in Dallas, Texas — www.prescs.org

- CC's Sisters — this group of Cindy's family members and friends raises money annually for the three-day Susan G. Komen sixty-mile walk with proceeds going to Komen www.the3day.org

- A portion of the proceeds from this book will be donated to the Susan G. Komen organization for the purpose of metastatic breast cancer research.

Table of Contents

Prologue

STEPPING INTO THE ARENA

"It is not the critic who counts; not the man who points out how
the strong man stumbles, or where the doer of deeds could
have done them better. The credit belongs to the man who is
actually in the arena, whose face is marred by dust and sweat
and blood; who strives valiantly; who errs, who comes short
again and again, because there is no effort without error and
shortcoming; but who does actually strive to do the deeds; who
knows great enthusiasms, the great devotions; who spends
himself in a worthy cause; who at the best knows in the end
the triumph of high achievement, and who at the worst, if he
fails, at least fails while daring greatly, so that his place shall
never be with those cold and timid souls who neither know
victory nor defeat."

— President Theodore Roosevelt

1

*T*his is the raw, powerful story of Cindy Colangelo, a woman who entered the arena and first learned and then taught essential life lessons as she bravely fought her battle with metastatic breast cancer.

A Miami native who found herself transplanted to the Lone Star State, Cindy was first diagnosed with cancer in 2001, when she was forty-three years old. After a cancerous lump was surgically removed, she was declared cancer free. Her lab results were good, and she referred to the whole process as just a "lump in the road."

She'd been married to Joe for six years; sons Jesse and Tony were ages fifteen and four. An excellent example of an accomplished single mom to Jesse prior to marrying Joe, Cindy had spent many years working in corporate relocation and had even started Destination Connection, providing relocation services as part of the William Rigg Real Estate Group, where she served as director of leasing. Later, as vice president of business development for Coldwell Banker in the Dallas–Fort Worth area, she often worked six days a week.

Within a few years of her breast cancer diagnosis, Cindy left corporate America and entered the non-profit world. There she played many roles, from executive director to events coordinator, putting together the large fundraising events that are so essential to non-profit organizations. Life was good at work and at home, and Cindy relished her many blessings.

In early 2009, a routine mammogram revealed her breast cancer had returned. She had been scheduled to go in for her eight-year check-up, the one that would declare her completely free of the dreaded disease, but instead of this joyful news, she was diagnosed with a recurrence of her cancer.

In the next year, with Joe, Jesse, and Tony by her side, Cindy underwent a double mastectomy, chemotherapy, radiation, Herceptin® therapy, and reconstructive surgery. By the end of this lengthy and challenging odyssey, she once again believed she had defeated her foe, but the experience changed her outlook and her career. Her drive and determination to work so hard decreased, and her faith and joy in helping others increased and morphed into consulting for non-profits. For a time, shaped by her work as an ombudsman and the bonds she formed volunteering, Cindy considered starting an organization centered around working with senior citizens. Simply put, she wanted to help those who were in need of love and support because she understood, at her core, the foundational importance of human connections.

One year after completing treatment for her second bout of cancer, Cindy found another lump just under the skin on her left breast. Since both breasts had been removed prior to reconstruction, Joe told her not to worry. It was probably just a piece of gauze from surgery working its way to the surface.

Cindy and her family clung to this hope until her diagnosis of stage IV metastatic breast cancer in January of 2011, which took her on a journey of hope and discovery to the end of her life.

Although Cindy ultimately lost her battle with breast cancer, throughout her life, she gave her time, her energy, and the very best of herself to everyone she knew. Her final gift was the journal she left behind on the website she developed with the help of the charitable organization CaringBridge®.

Written over the course of more than four years as her cancer came, went, returned, and settled in for the long haul, Cindy began her online journal in 2009 with encouragement from her family. The idea was to give her a way to keep her friends updated on the details of her treatment without spending inordinate amounts of time on the telephone, repeating herself. As so often happens with writing, keeping this online journal helped Cindy as much as it helped her readers. She had scores of followers, some of whom she'd never met. When she passed away, her family received many notes from people who had read her words, were inspired by her positive thoughts and entertaining stories, and were heartbroken at the conclusion of her earthly journey.

Candy-Coated Chunk of Granite: The Inspiring Journey of One Woman's Valiant Battle with Metastatic Breast Cancer is drawn primarily from Cindy's journal entries. It is a book of inspiration in the face of insurmountable odds, emotional power in the face of physical weakness, and a winning spirit in the face of the ultimate defeat. Cindy Colangelo's legacy can be found on every page.

Even as she suffered the effects of cancer and the drugs that battled within her, Cindy stood tall and fought with courage. Though loving family and friends surrounded her, in the end, she had to fight her battle alone. She did so valiantly.

In her journal entries, Cindy talks openly and honestly about her physical and emotional struggles, how she chose to face them, and the lessons she learned along the way. She accepted that she needed help, and she sought spiritual and medical guidance wherever she could find it. She read voraciously. She volunteered for cancer drug trials. She raised money for cancer research even as the very organization that would help her buy a few more months with her family and friends came under fire.

Cindy's family culled through more than one hundred journal entries, some of them quite lengthy, to choose the passages that best represent her spirit, her tenacity, and her positive attitude — in short, the story of her life. Sprinkled throughout *Candy-Coated Chunk of Granite* is the back story about Cindy — her life, her loves, her cancer, and her battle to live — to help readers understand the context of her actions and the true strength they reveal.

In the fifty-five years of her life, Cindy served in many roles, including wife, mother, sister, daughter, aunt, friend, full-time volunteer, cancer advocate, and teacher. In each role, she provided leadership, strength, and inspiration.

One of the key life lessons Cindy taught those who knew her is that it's not all about you. On the contrary, it's about what you do for others.

Yes, she wanted the cancer trials to cure her cancer. However, she considered it a "win" if the doctors and researchers learned something from her participation that would help future generations of patients.

Yes, she hoped the money she helped Susan G. Komen raise would enable scientists to find a cure for her cancer. However, she was happy that cures for different cancers were emerging from the research this organization conducted.

Yes, she wanted to live. However, she grew stronger in her faith in God even as her battle with cancer came to an end. Ultimately, she wanted to support her family and live strong in her faith. She cried in private and turned her sorrow into smiles for those who looked to her for inspiration and direction.

When Cindy learned she had only a few weeks left to live, her family asked her what she wanted to do in that time. Consult spiritual teachers? Travel to an exotic location? Make a private lifelong dream come true?

None of the above. Cindy wanted a party. Not just any party. She wanted to invite everyone she knew and loved. By the time you finish reading her journal, you will realize exactly how big an undertaking this would be for those around her.

But that's jumping the gun. A whole lot happened before that final party. In the following pages, you will read about the battle of a lifetime and the hope that sustained Cindy as she lived to the end of her earthly life. This journey of hope is a testament to Cindy's unquenchable spirit; it's a story of inspiration and life-affirming lessons about how she courageously faced her battle with cancer.

She faced that battle with family, friends, and faith. In the end, so much was gained as a result of the battle Cindy ultimately lost: from the deepening of essential relationships to the transformative personal and spiritual growth experienced by many through the inspiring example she set in her continuation to do more and do it better. In short, as unexpected as it sounds, what Cindy left behind was greater because of her cancer.

Chapter One
THE ART OF THE PIVOT

"For my mom, breast cancer resulted in inspiration, hope, and strength. Without my mom in my life, I can honestly say I would have no faith."

— Tony Colangelo, Cindy's youngest son

*I*n January of 2009, shortly after undergoing what she expected to be a routine mammogram, Cindy traveled to Houston to visit her sister Ellen and help complete the paperwork to establish Ellen's new company. The two women were wrangling with a complicated tax form and laughing at how frustrating it was when the phone rang.

The caller was Cindy's doctor.

Cindy's cancer, first diagnosed and believed to be cured in 2001, had returned.

"The sadness we felt was like a punch in the stomach," Ellen recalls. "At the same time, the will to fight was immediate."

Cindy and Ellen had always been close. When Cindy was undergoing a difficult divorce and custody battle with Jesse's dad, Ellen had moved from Florida to Dallas to live with Cindy and Jesse, an arrangement that lasted several years.

By 2009, Ellen was married and living in Houston with her husband, Drew, and their four-year-old son Andrew, nicknamed IV. Cindy was IV's godmother; Ellen was Jesse's godmother. The two families spent most holidays together and traveled across Texas to see each other as often as possible.

At this time, Jesse was about to graduate from college at the University of North Texas and was living on his own in a condo near downtown Dallas. He had a great relationship with his mother and visited often, and it didn't hurt that a meal and the washing machine were always available.

It never bothered Cindy that Jesse still brought his laundry home for her to do; she realized the day would come when that no longer happened.

Tony was now twelve. A happy kid who did well in school, he was busy with soccer, band, and running around with his friends. He was involved in sports, loved video games, and had a strong bond with his dad. Cindy loved this; she also loved seeing Joe's relationship with Jesse continue to grow.

Proud of her boys and the people they were becoming, Cindy wasn't about to let cancer derail her plans. Instead, she embraced what her friends and family called "the art of the pivot." Even while her breast cancer treatments resumed and she began posting journal entries on her CaringBridge website, she insisted that life go on as usual, with holidays, birthdays, and other events celebrated normally.

Believing her cancer was curable, Cindy used her journal to offer readers her take on life, love, and the importance of bearing this challenge with faith, grace, and courage. She turned her back on negativity and instead focused on her many blessings, as this first series of journal entries reveals.

March 26, 2009

Wow, bear with me. My first journal entry, and what a good day to report! It took me a while to start this journal, but thanks to the nudging of some very special people, I decided this might be the best way to keep people updated. I'd rather have a blog of famous Cindy jokes, but hopefully I can weave some in here and there.

Today was a great, great day. I am so touched by the messages left for me. I feel like Dorothy in The Wizard of Oz *when she closes her eyes and says, "I do believe, I do believe, I do believe." Thanks to all for believing in the power of love and prayer!*

April 3, 2009

Okay, so I didn't go blonde. Didn't want to be another big-chested blonde Texas girl like that stereotype people have of us. And I mean no offense to all the blonde Texas women I love! I did go to a sassy copper/ golden-brown color, but first came the hair removal ...

I'm not bald yet, but I had all my hair cut off yesterday and am showing a lot of face. I must admit that with the first snip, I had second thoughts. But as my new BFF, Don, continued, it became easier and easier. I figure I'm going to be without any hair at all very soon, so this will be a nice transition. Brings me back to when I was about six years old and the Beatles invasion was beginning ... Everyone was going to a pixie cut, the Welsh girls included. Mom took my sisters and me to "Mr. Charles," who whacked off all our hair. I'm not sure we were very happy about it, but what Mom said went. I just hope people don't mistake me for a boy this time!

Don was wonderful, commenting on how nice I look with short hair (he has to, that's his job), and I left his shop with my new do and my new accessory I fondly call "Sassy." You will get to meet Sassy soon, so get ready!

So many of you have asked what you can do to help ... Cooking, driving, running errands, etc. To tell you the truth, I feel great! I know that may change next week with the chemo starting, but right now I feel pretty normal (whatever that is). I would actually feel guilty taking help at this point when there are so many people who truly need help. If that changes, I promise I will reach out.

But I can't pass up the opportunity to share how you might help indirectly. What I have really become aware of is the power of the love I have received from each of you. Your wishes, cards, and prayers are encouraging and inspiring and very much treasured. I don't know that I would be in this frame of mind without all of you!

As you know, through all of this, I have been working from home and focusing on two non-profits, Senior Adult Services and Dallas Afterschool Network. I've become very aware that many people aren't lucky enough to have the incredible support system I have. Instead of doing something for me, please consider reaching out to those who would love to have a meal delivered, a ride offered, or a card sent.

April 11, 2009

After watching my hair fall out this week and leaving a trail wherever I go, I've decided to get the old noggin shaved. Cutting it short wasn't that tough, though my ears stick out a little more than I remembered. My best friend Babs suggested I tape them back at night when I sleep, but I'm opting out of that. (Maybe I'll try a little putty; that wouldn't be as obvious.)

I'll have company as I get my new look ... Babs and Trisha are going with me. Trisha, our drill sergeant in boot camp and our inspiration to keep fit, will be shaving her head along with me, and we're going to see if we can talk B. into it as well. Don't know how that will work with her professional image, but maybe it will start a trend!

I've been watching videos on how to tie bandanas. I still have my "Sassy" wig, too. The thought of having a bald head is kind of scary. I'm not sure how it will impact my self-image, but I'll keep you posted. I will also add to my list of prayers to have fewer windy days. I've already had to chase Sassy across a parking lot, as it blew out of my hands the first day as I made my way to the car. Having it blow off a bald head could be a completely different type of embarrassment!

So far so good with the after-effects of this chemo. And it's Easter weekend, one of my favorite times of the year. The flowers are blooming, the air is crisp, and the skies are blue. Springtime in Dallas can be beautiful. It's kind of appropriate that I'm going bald this weekend. I'll have my own version of an Easter egg on top. I might even add some colorful design in honor of the day.

May 6, 2009

Had another mini chemo cocktail today and met with the physician assistant. All in all, I'm doing great. Had a temperature, so got some medicine to fight off infection. Was starting to feel a little whiny until I met the neatest couple at the hospital. The woman saw what I was reading, the incredibly suspenseful 90 Days to Success in Fundraising, and we started talking. She told me about all her years of volunteering in emergency rooms.

14

She said that a doctor once taught her how to see red blood as gray. To this day, because she sees gray when she sees blood, she doesn't have a problem with blood.

Her sweet husband had to go back to the "cocktail lounge," and you could hear him greeting those around him. They've been married fifty-five years, and for the last seven years, they've had to visit the clinic once a week for his blood work. About every three weeks, they go to the hospital so he can get a transfusion that lasts from about 8:00 a.m. until 4:30 p.m. Her comment to me when she heard him coming back was, "Fifty-five years, and he still makes me smile!"

That helped Miss Whiny Butt here to an attitude adjustment.

May 11, 2009

Wow, is this cancer/chemo stuff weird! A week ago, I felt like I wouldn't have the energy to make it through another week, much less another couple of months. Today, yowza! What a great day, and I have no lack of energy. It's like the healing fairy visited last night and sprinkled her magical dust, and now I'm like new! A little lopsided and bald, but feeling pretty darned good.

I got out today, met some neat people, got caught up, and then came home and cleaned out a closet. And I'm still going. And yesterday, wow! Spending the day with my three guys was wonderful, and Mother's Day was a little more special this year. Cancer helps you appreciate the simple things, especially time together. I'm thrilled with the garden clippers I got. No more ragged flower stems for me!

I really think the biggest part of this healing process has been the support, prayers, and love of those around me. Just when I need a boost, I get a card or call or message and am good to go. Again, that little healing fairy must be out there sprinkling her healing dust. Boy, do I thank God for that fairy! And for my family! And my friends! And my faith!

May 26, 2009

My sweet son Jesse accompanied me to my last fill-up, and we spent most of the time snoozing, me in my comfortable chair, and he with his head against the wall. The doctor's report came back and he said I'm doing great, that my blood work looks good. I'm just sailing through (with a little motion sickness at times). In just about five weeks, I'll be done with this portion. I'm counting the days.

When you're in the middle of it, it's not as bad as you think it's going to be. Besides, the doctors and nurses these days are incredible.

June 7, 2009

Saturday morning, I joined two friends to do the Susan G. Komen Race for the Cure. I had to get up earlier than I wanted to, but once I did, I was glad. It's always amazing to see how many people have been impacted by breast cancer, and this wasn't even the big event for our area. It was a gorgeous morning, with a cool breeze blowing and the sun shining brightly. I've always been touched by the women who are obviously fresh in their battle with this disease, and this year, here I was, marching bald in pink with dear friends before attending Joe's company party!

The day wore me out, so we spent our Saturday evening chillin' (as Jesse would say) on the couch and watching Titanic. *Probably not a good choice for someone who will be on a cruise ship in about a month, but I don't expect we'll have to worry about any icebergs in the Caribbean!*

Today I was able to attend an event for cancer survivors, and the real reason I went was to hear Suzie Humphreys speak. She has such a way of seeing the humor in life. I first heard her speak about eighteen years ago. Her words impacted me then, and I wanted to let her know. Her words today had special meaning, too. She is seventy-two years young and a wonderful soul!

June 12, 2009

I'm counting down the days until we take a short Florida break, and then I'll be looking forward to the celebratory cruise with Joe after my last treatment. Have I mentioned that I cannot wait?

Then, in August, it's on to a real celebration, Jesse's college graduation! There were times when I had my doubts that I'd see this day, and I am so excited. He did it, we did it, and he's got so much ahead of him!

All my boys have been so wonderful throughout this whole process. Jesse has joined me for my last two treatments, and I think he's caught the attention of a couple of the nurses. It's been a special time for us, even if we've dozed through some of it.

All in all, I feel so blessed every day! The simplest gestures mean so much. I have a long list of thank yous to send out once I'm at full operating capacity, but if I could reach out and hug everyone who has shared their love, I would be hugging a good long while.

Come to think of it, that might be a good way to fight arm flab. I think I'll give it a go. If you see me coming with outstretched arms, get ready. Not only am I sharing my love, I'm working off this middle-aged arm flab. Don't fight the cause!

June 24, 2009

I carry a daily journal almost everywhere I go. (No, I haven't gone electronic yet.) In it are the words, "The beauty of life lies in its imperfection." I glanced at this quote today and realized how true it is. Beauty definitely has been redefined for me. Am I comfortable with my bald white head? No, but it isn't as shocking as I initially thought it would be. The other changes to my body are kind of growing on me, too. I've learned how to perform magic with hats, scarves, and wigs as well as to make helpful clothing adjustments. I'm employing "smoke and mirrors" these days, to borrow a favorite quote from a friend from my real estate days.

A few things I've discovered:

- *It's all about the love. I wouldn't trade my family and friends for any amount of money or fame. (Although there is one person I might think twice about. Got you all thinking, haven't I?)*

- *Simple pleasures are the best. I love watching dolphins swim through the water while sitting on the beach.*

- *Raw oysters and cold beer. Especially when enjoyed with people you love. (Okay, maybe that's another simple pleasure.)*

- *The smallest gesture can mean so much. Many wonderful gestures have touched me. I hope I am able to pay them forward.*

- *Frozen daiquiris are great healers. Especially for the blisters you get in your mouth from the chemo. The frozenness soothes, and the alcohol cures. Thanks to my incredible Uncle Gene for this tip.*

- *Life is wonderful! I have always known this, but it takes on new meaning these days.*

The hard part of the journey is almost over, and my friends and family along the way have been awesome. We will celebrate the imperfection of life soon!

July 4, 2009

Happy Fourth of July! Independence Day takes on new meaning this year. I've always loved fireworks (except when I was really little and the loud booms kind of scared me), and I'm ready to start fireworks of my own again, really soon!

I am so pumped to be looking forward. I can't wait for fewer cloudy-headed days and more energy to move forward on a daily basis, and I'm lining up projects! As I mentioned, a cruise with Joe will celebrate his birthday earlier this year as well as the completion of chemo, my oldest baby turns twenty-three and graduates from college in August, and Tony is honing his performance skills on his dad's old trumpet, so I'm sure there will be musical events in the near future.

There will be more doctor's visits and five weeks of radiation (but that's going to be a breeze), continuing drug treatments with the "friendly" drug (but that's a breeze, too), and then welcoming the "new permanent kids on the block," hopefully in time for Christmas. The word on the street from many is to prepare for dark and curly ... I will take the dark, as the little specks I have coming in look mighty gray!

But, oh, Independence Day! I can't wait to celebrate just that. We have the ability to choose how we live (within reason). We're all dealt different circumstances, and it's up to us to choose how we respond. It isn't the great big pleasures that count the most; it's making a great deal out of the little ones.

July 21, 2009

I'm settling back into reality after a fabulous trip to the Bahamas. Wow, was it wonderful to be away and escape for a while. The weather was perfect, and Joe and I really enjoyed the sun and relaxation. My biggest challenge was maintaining my headgear on the top deck of the ship. (Almost lost Sassy once and tried to stay on the lower levels when outside.) Also had to figure out how to snorkel with a head covering. After some creative placement, I was able to pull a mask over a bandana. I kind of look like a little monkey now ... My face is tan and my head is really white.

I feel wonderful, and the chemo is running its course. I do have some lingering side effects. My nails are splitting, my eyelashes and eyebrows are very sparse, and my hair is still MIA. Good thing clumped mascara is in style, right? Those few remaining eyelashes are taking the heat for their missing comrades.

Joe thinks I should shave the few hairs I have so that once it all starts growing back it comes in evenly. He was chasing me down with his clippers yesterday, trying to convince me it will be fun. Ellie suggested that I really set the mood by lighting some candles, playing some slow music, and letting him shave my head. Sounds romantic, doesn't it?

I had the chance to do a walk for the cure on an upper deck of the cruise ship. It's kind of different doing a fundraising walk on the open seas. I think that's how all my future events will be held!

I do realize how blessed I am and what a good situation I have. I'm counting the days until things are back to "normal," while others will never know "normal" again. I wonder why I was chosen to experience the easy route while others have so many more challenges ahead of them. I definitely plan to use these experiences for something good.

I'm not sure how often I'll be updating this site now that the bad days are behind me. I don't expect the radiation to be a major event, nor should the Herceptin treatments; treatment will be more of a scheduling challenge than anything. I'm grateful for the chance to share this journey with you and for the wonderful thoughts and prayers you've shared with me. You've given me the strength to push forward, and every word and gesture has made a difference. The sticks of gum that came in cards to take away the metallic taste from chemo, the home-cooked meals, the prayer cards, the books, the music, the pjs, the bandanas, the phone calls, the teddy bears, the flowers, the notes, the company ...

Everyone should be so lucky. I have felt the love, and I think I hear Gloria Gaynor in the background, getting ready to break into song. I have survived!

July 26, 2009

Today has turned out to be a tough one, emotionally, although I'm still well on my way to recovery and being finished with all this stuff. I received word today that cancer claimed the life of a wonderful woman with whom I worked in my previous life, before I met Joe. As I celebrate my recovery, I can't help but ask, "Why me?" Why are some taken and some bruised for a while and others spared completely? Why must some spend years suffering the effects of devastating diseases, never to know the happiness and joy that so many others experience each day?

Yesterday I spent my morning with a group of brave people who have been impacted by Huntington disease. Many have lost not one member of their family but as many as eight, with other family members at risk or just waiting for the effects to start presenting themselves. This is a devastating disease that claims families. Imagine having Parkinson's, ALS, and Alzheimer's all in one. I talked to a woman who lost her mom, sister, nephew, stepsisters, and more. I talked to another woman who is the caregiver for her husband and brother-in-law and just learned her daughter has the gene for the disease. I talked to another woman whose father and uncle committed suicide to spare their families the heartbreak of spending years watching their loved one slowly deteriorate. They all hold hope that through their work and action, a cure will one day be found.

My point is, there are so many people loaded with burdens. You never know when things may turn and your life may be impacted. CaringBridge has been a great tool for me to keep you all updated and for you to shower me with love and support to help keep me looking forward. I pray we all become "caring bridges" for those who need our love and support.

August 23, 2009

I have just returned from one of my walks. The opportunity to reflect while listening to music always leaves me inspired. I'm doing a lot of reflecting as we finish up celebrating Jesse's graduation. It has been wonderful, and having my energy back has allowed me to fully participate and enjoy all the family and friends who joined in the fun.

I've also been able to reach out to several women who are either about to go through a similar experience or who are in the middle of it. The unknown is scary, and as I found, the simplest gesture can make all the difference in the world. I hope I am able to give back what was given to me. Things happen, and it's how you deal with them that makes the difference. Being surrounded by wonderful people surely helps to make that difference. And, as I've said many times, keeping the faith is important.

Which leads me to one of the songs I listened to while thinking about gathering to celebrate Jesse's accomplishment. Watching him cross the stage to receive his diploma, seeing the young man he's become, the pride and love Joe and I feel when we look at him, the fun we shared with my sisters and their families plus my parents, cousins, and friends …

I don't know if Billy Joel meant the words to "Keeping the Faith" the way I interpret them today, but what the heck. They seem to touch home:

If it seems like I've been lost in let's remember

If you think I'm feeling older and missing my younger days

Oh, then you should have known me much better

'Cause my past is something that never got in my way

Oh no

Still I would not be here now if I never had the hunger

And I'm not ashamed to say the wild boys were my friends

Oh, 'cause I never felt the desire 'til their music set me on fire

And then I was saved, yeah

That's why I'm keeping the faith

Yeah, yeah, yeah, yeah, keeping the faith ...

(BILLY JOEL *lyrics are property and copyright of JoelSongs.*)

Keep the faith!

October 3, 2009

Okay, friends, here's the situation. My recovery is going extremely well. Breast removal: done. Bad chemo: done. Radiation: done. Breast burn: done. Herceptin treatments: ongoing till March (but no sweat). Permanent breast reconstruction: delayed until January (boo). Hair regrowth: slow!

In my whole cancer journey, one of the consequences I most dreaded was losing my hair. It isn't just me, either. I've had many conversations with women who feel the same way, over the growth of something that on other parts of our body we pay money to get rid of. Isn't it funny that the hair we don't want seems to grow exponentially faster than the hair we do want? I find myself thinking about the shallowness of it all. If beauty does really come from within, why am I stressing over external things that don't really matter?

25

I'm working up the courage to put the scarves, hats, and wigs away permanently. In light of Breast Cancer Awareness Month, I think I could carry a message that echoes words I have spoken so frequently: "In the big scheme of things, it doesn't really matter."

Hair, manicured fingernails, and beautiful breasts don't define your femininity or who you are; the inside spirit does.

I'm just not sure I'm ready to be the messenger.

October 21, 2009

I've done it! After walking on Saturday with so many others in support of finding a cure for breast cancer, I've spent the afternoon about town without a head covering. Now I must admit, I had some of that gray touched up before I let the inhibitions go, but the old head is now out there, ready for the world.

So, another chapter is behind me. I have a ways to go before the total package is back at 100%, but slowly we are making headway (no pun intended).

Moving on to bigger and better!

By October of 2009, Cindy again believed that she was cured. She'd done everything right, everything she was supposed to, including making the difficult decision to have her breasts removed.

Although she understood the necessity of this, a part of her struggled with it.

It was also hard for her to lose her hair, not so much because of vanity but because she knew people would likely treat her differently. Simply put, she didn't want cancer to define her.

On the other hand, Cindy was proud that she'd had reconstructive surgery. She loved going out and buying new bras, putting on a sexy dress, and having the chest to wear it. She took a trip to Las Vegas during this time with Joe, Ellen, Drew, Jesse, and one of Jesse's buddies, and they had a wonderful time exploring the town.

Joe and Cindy also traveled to Italy in 2010. Their friends had been planning the trip for ten months, and for much of that time, it wasn't clear whether Cindy would be able to go. Eventually, after finalizing care arrangements for Tony, who was only thirteen, Joe surprised Cindy with plane tickets. With a group of twenty wonderful friends, some old and some new, they shared villas on a hillside overlooking the amazing Amalfi coast. Because Cindy wasn't suffering any serious side effects from the medicines at this time, they were able to walk, eat, drink, and thoroughly enjoy themselves on this bucket-list trip.

Meanwhile, Cindy, Ellen, and their families continued to share birthdays and holidays. As usual, Cindy included friends who didn't have family at her annual "no-kin din" Thanksgiving. Her favorite holiday activity was to make everyone at the table share what they were thankful for. Although this was excruciatingly painful for some people, Cindy relished the opportunity to share her feelings. Secretly, she might have even loved putting people on the spot and watching them squirm a little.

After her reconstructive surgery, she went on to have her temporary breast implants replaced with permanent ones and went through another surgery to remove the port through which she received Herceptin. In the following entry, Cindy signs off from her CaringBridge website. Believing this journal entry will be her last, she offers what she expects to be her final thoughts.

May 16, 2010

It has been a long but short journey, if that makes any sense. Looking back, it seems like a long time since I first received word of this adventure I would be setting out on, but as I sit here today, it also seems just like yesterday.

I look back at pictures taken during the past year and can't believe I made it through the rough days of chemo and survived without hair. To see me now, nothing outwardly identifies me as a cancer survivor ... The hair is growing back, the port has been removed, and my body has been recreated to look almost like new. But underneath it all, my heart has changed.

I hope that as I continue to get back to a normal life, where doctor's visits don't dictate my schedule, I'm able to remember the important lessons I've learned along the way.

One is a most important lesson I was first taught by my dad, who told me, "Always tell people that you care about them because a day may come when you can't."

I have tried to live by these words, but now I'll take them one step further: don't ever hesitate to say something nice or to offer words of encouragement, even if you think they're insignificant. You don't know how much a simple gesture of kindness can mean, but I do. I have experienced it firsthand.

With my last surgery over, all that remains are a few stitches to be removed and the gauze and tape to be eliminated. I want you all to know that the thoughts you've shared these past months have brought me comfort and encouragement. I hope never to forget how blessed I am, even when I once again struggle with the critically important "bad hair days" coming my way. If you've seen the thick bushy hair that has replaced my previous hair, you know those days are coming. I also hope I can avoid rushing to judgment when someone challenges my patience. I know I've challenged the patience of those around me these last few months when I operated off-kilter. Or, as I loving call it, when I was "discom-boob-ulated."

And so I sign off from this CaringBridge site for the last time. Wishing you much love and happiness ...

Unfortunately, this would not be Cindy's last bout with the cancer that would ultimately take her life. In just eight months, the cancer would return, a stronger foe than before, challenging her to pivot once again and return to the arena. Not surprisingly, Cindy quickly resumed writing her CaringBridge journal entries.

Chapter Two

LIFE LESSONS FROM
THE FRONT LINES

"Even though she was going through one of the
toughest things one can, she was able to set that aside
and appreciate the good things in every single day."

—Jesse DeAnda, Cindy's oldest son

*A*fter a sweet hiatus, Cindy's cancer returned in January of 2011.

"I couldn't believe it," Joe said. "I was sure the doctors had left something inside of her, like gauze or something, and that it had taken a while to work its way to the surface. I could not, or maybe would not, believe the cancer was back."

Cindy was deeply concerned when she found a lump in her left breast, and Ellen was stunned. How could cancer return in a breast that had been removed and reconstructed with permanent implants?

Within days, Cindy, Ellen, and Joe had gathered up the paperwork detailing Cindy's history and sent it to several highly recommended doctors and facilities. They wanted to know which oncology doctors, hospitals, and research facilities were best at treating HER2+, Cindy's particular type of cancer.

The answer arrived the week of Super Bowl XLV, which was being held in Cindy's hometown of Dallas. The doctor they needed to see was in Houston, where Ellen and her family lived, at the MD Anderson Cancer Center.

In full pivot once again, Cindy resumed writing in her journal on the CaringBridge website. The many journal entries that follow show how she faced this new challenge with her trademark indomitable courage and unceasing commitment to help others while loving the friends and family around her.

January 30, 2011

Heading into 2011, I was excited to start the year completely free of the disease that had been such a part of my life for the previous two years. Unfortunately, as the saying goes, God had different plans.

Preparing for a fun New Year's Eve celebration with close friends, I discovered another lump in my left breast. After the standard routine — sonogram, mammogram, and biopsy — we learned that surgery would be necessary, at which time we discovered the cancer had returned. Who would have thought after the mastectomy and subsequent chemo and radiation therapy that anything could survive? Apparently, it was suppressed temporarily and not completely eradicated. Luckily, the tumor was close enough to the surface that I detected it pretty quickly. Hopefully we've caught it early.

We have learned that while the cancer is still local, it has moved outside the breast and there are several "areas of concern." Joe and I met with our team of doctors here to discuss the next step, and with the help of my sister and her husband, will travel to MD Anderson this week to consult with other specialists. Once we have a second opinion and agreement on the treatment plan, we will begin.

While this has caught us totally by surprise, we remain positive and faithful that God will pull us through again. We ask for your prayers, love, and support as we start another journey in beating this disease!

An ice storm hit just about the time of Cindy's appointment at MD Anderson. For football fans, this was the same ice storm that led to a disaster at the new Texas Stadium, injuring several workmen trying to finish up in time for the Super Bowl.

Thousands of people were flying in from all over the country for the big game, but flights were difficult to find and roads all but impassable. Many businesses, including the hospital, sent staff home.

"We were one of two patients the doctor didn't cancel that day," Ellen recalled. "He said to us, 'I don't know who you know, but you had to pull some serious strings to get me here today.'"

The sisters were very excited to see the top oncologist specializing in Cindy's cancer type until they heard his diagnosis.

"You have metastatic breast cancer," Dr. Valero told Cindy. "This will kill you. I cannot cure you, but I can help prolong your life." He added, "This is a marathon, not a sprint."

The two sisters felt indescribable shock. Nonetheless, the doctor's words inspired Cindy to do all she could to help those who still had a chance at full recovery.

What Cindy did was make a difference. She flew home to tell Joe in person what she and Ellen had learned in Houston. Even if she couldn't be cured, she was determined to do all she could to raise money for a cure and would offer herself for any drug trials she was qualified for in order to buy as much time as possible with those she loved. Cindy flew back to Houston on Super Bowl

Sunday in order to be present for tests and consults on Monday.

She finally understood the severity and finality of her disease. She was frightened, but in her typical fashion, she put her fear in a box and moved on, projecting a positive attitude and exemplifying the art of courageous living. While Cindy insisted that her cancer would not define her, she gracefully stood in the spotlight it pointed on her and her family as they learned the lessons that only a life and death battle can teach.

For his part, Joe watched as his wife bravely faced each day with grace and dignity, despite cancer's best efforts to strip her of both. "How do you go on with an anvil suspended over your head by a fraying rope?" he asked. "I don't know how she did it, but she was the one who kept everyone going. She knew how to put a shell around the cancer and just keep going. She chose to be happy. She was our rock."

Jesse and Tony were a huge support to their parents. Their faith and belief in God guided them, and they wanted to be strong for their mom. They received their strength from her, and they wanted to reflect her positive attitude and abundance of determination back to her. They knew they had a battle before them, but they were very hopeful.

Ellen explained that whenever Cindy felt helpless, she would look around and see what she could learn from the situation and how she could use those lessons to help others. "Helping others, talking with others, made Cindy feel useful. Everyone talked about how Cindy impacted their lives and inspired them, but I don't think they had any idea how much she thrived on helping others."

Cindy wrote the journal entries that follow with the knowledge that her cancer could not be cured and that her best and only option was to pursue treatments that might prolong her life a few precious months. Determined to make each day count, Cindy used her journal to document all the life lessons and blessings that only someone facing the uncertainty of tomorrow can fully understand.

February 8, 2011

Friends, after a crazy week of appointments, consultations, testing, and weather, I am back in Dallas. I am so grateful for the encouraging messages of love and support from so many of you; you will never know how they help me keep my head in this race, a race that will be longer than we initially thought. Every word, prayer, and gesture makes such an impact on me, and people I have never met are playing a part in mapping out our future game plan.

Along with Joe monitoring my diet and attitude, my incredible sister and brother-in-law have been my support in Houston, helping me get in to see people I would never have been able to meet otherwise. Networking does pay off, and Ellen's friends in Houston have come through. Dr. Valero will be working with my doctor in Dallas to help direct this plan of attack.

One of Ellen's best friends actually works for the drug company that produces what has been billed a "miracle drug," and we are doing what we can to see if I'm a candidate. Things are looking good, and if everything pans out, I may undergo treatment in San Antonio for this clinical trial that has been recommended by both my doctors.

February 14, 2011

I was able to see my doctor in Dallas on Wednesday and compare notes from my trip to Houston. If anyone ever finds themselves in my position, I hope they're supported by the kind of people I have in my life. Ellen and Drew are my awesome Houston team. They kept my spirits up, provided the hugs I needed, and had the research going so we had "real time" info when we needed it. When I returned to Dallas, Ellen kept at it, providing information that would be helpful in determining where to go next.

And technology! What a gift when it's used for good, and it's been working overtime on my behalf. While I was meeting with the doctor in his office, Ellie sent me an email of a new trial study that's available. I showed him my Blackberry and clicked on the link, and he realized this study is perfect for me and that I can be treated in Dallas! After the letdown of realizing the previous study wasn't a match, just that quickly we had another option. And while my doctor was in and out of the office gathering additional information, my Houston doctor called and gave his blessing!

We've made it through the insurance company's approval process after a couple of bumps and are ready to start this clinical study. I will have surgery on Wednesday to put in a port, some tests on Thursday, and additional tests Friday. Many of these duplicate what I had to do in Houston, but we need to have a good baseline for comparison so we can determine whether the treatments are having an effect.

Hopefully, the first treatment will be administered by Tuesday or Wednesday of next week so we can start killing this cancer! I'm told I should not lose my hair (yeah!), so I've scheduled an appointment for a "recovery" hairdo. There are some things you just can't do without.

I'm also hoping my port is in the right side so I can wear the awesome one-shoulder top Joe gave me for Christmas. Sometimes these cancer treatments just don't cooperate with fashion!

Special love to all my angels on this special Valentine's Day.

Every day was a rollercoaster of sorts, bringing new information, new choices, new hope.

Joe explained, "It was amazing to literally be in the doctor's office pulling up clinical trials on the Internet, some the doctor wasn't even aware of. You can research available clinical trials on your own and be proactive with your treatment plan. So much is happening in the research field that the doctors on the front lines sometimes can't keep up."

Ellen added, "We learned about several clinical trials from the doctor at MD Anderson. I researched them and tried to see which Cindy might qualify for. Because of her previous treatments, some were automatically eliminated. As we learned about one that was a possibility, the location or timing wouldn't be good, or her doctors would determine that the lines of treatment she'd already had would negate the results of the trial. The advances in cancer treatments are constantly changing, so it took pure determination to find the next trial or treatment. Cindy decided to go with this particular treatment because she could stay home and not have to travel to another city."

The comfort and location were perfect, yet as the following journal entry shows, new developments continued to alter Cindy's treatment plans.

February 18, 2011

Well, things are literally changing by the hour, or perhaps I should say minute.

I was preparing to go to the hospital today for two more tests when I received a call from the research manager, Mary, at my doctor's office. She'd called late yesterday after learning about another new clinical study that will be opening in a few weeks here in Dallas. This study involves the drug TDM 1 that has been called a "miracle drug" for breast cancer and is similar to the study in San Antonio I was originally shooting for before learning I didn't qualify. Mary is someone I met just last week, and she has been wonderful in helping me through this crazy process of figuring out what is going to kick this cancer's butt. Although her office isn't involved in this study, she thought I would be a perfect candidate.

I spoke with the research manager at UT Southwestern, and after listening to my history, she agreed that I would be a good candidate. The compassion and empathy she conveyed were reassuring, and we've started the process to get me enrolled in this new study, which should start March 4.

No tests today due to this newest development. I will be meeting with another doctor at UT Southwestern, hopefully next week, to confirm that I truly am a good candidate for this clinical trial study for a drug that both my doctors feel is the best choice if possible to get.

Stay posted ...

March 13, 2011

Monday, time for a routine echo and Thursday a complete echo (whatever that means), and then Friday a big day, meeting with Dr. Haley to discuss our plan of action. Then, a week from Monday, my first treatment. Yeah! The attack will begin! Sprinkle in the midst of all that spring break for Tony, happy birthday for Joey, happy St. Patrick's Day with green beer, visits with some dear old friends (no, not old in that way!), and much more. There will be a lot of happiness and celebration mixed in with some discomfort, all contributing to happily ever after!

Babs and I had our first meeting in preparation for the Komen three-day walk scheduled for November 6, 7, and 8. It's going to be an undertaking but all for a good cause. Breast cancer research has taken on new meaning now that I find myself right in the middle of it.

March 26, 2011

Happy Saturday, and it's a beautiful one here in Dallas. Blue skies, tulips blooming, warm temps, not too hot (yet), and I've almost completed my first week post treatment. Yeah!

Monday was a long day. Started at 9:00 a.m. and finished at 5:00 p.m. Because it was the first treatment, they took it slowly, and I think I got a little extra kick to start the process. After each treatment, they had to observe me to make sure I had no reactions as well as to take vitals. At any one time, we had seven to eight people in the room.

Julie, my research coordinator, already a good, good friend, and Eddie, the sweetest nurse, were in charge of

41

the treatment, Julie directing and Eddie administering the drugs. Since I have a port, I didn't have to endure a lot of sticking and poking, just a simple stick at the beginning of the process. This was relatively painless, since I applied a pain relief cream before show time.

Other people were observing, including a nurse intern from TCU who happens to be a huge Tim Tebow fan. As you can imagine, this intern ranked high in my book! Another nurse poked her head into the room, and of course I had my personal support team consisting of Joe, Jesse, and one of my best friends from Florida along with her friend. To say I was in good hands is putting it mildly. Other than the day being long and the chair uncomfortable, everything went smoothly.

We have been blessed with meals from friends, cookies from Joe's co-workers, flowers from my sister, and much love and support from so many. It really helps pass these days and keep our outlook bright.

Tony is keeping us hopping. He made his school's soccer team (yeah!) and is performing at the Morton H. Meyerson Symphony Center in Dallas today with his chorus group. I try to get out as much as I can to enjoy the fun ... Tony's soccer games, Pokeno, dinner with friends, poolside gatherings. Although I may not be as active as in the past, Joe says it really recharges me. We will continue to do what we can, when we can, though no dancing on tabletops for a while.

I've also pulled away from anything that requires a commitment. I never know what I'll be able to deliver, and I can't deal with the thought of letting someone down.

I'm looking forward to the three-day walk in November. Barbara and I have pulled together a team we call CC's Sisters. The "CC" comes from my initials. We are looking for walkers and contributors and will be planning some fundraisers in the next few months. I guess my years of experience might finally come in handy to help a cause that personally impacts me. I am so thankful for cancer research and proud that I might be able to personally testify to the benefits of that research. What better mission than to help save lives, literally?

May 13, 2011

I can't believe that in less than a week, I'll be undergoing tests to see what is really going on with the Pac Man Cancer Killers! Since my last treatment, I've been able to spend some time in Miami with my family, celebrating my niece's graduation and Mother's Day with my mom and sisters.

Although I was away from my boys, I was able to score an early Mother's Day lunch with Jesse along with some delicious designer "cake balls" (yummy!) before I went. And I came home to a long overdue painted bathroom, newly planted herbs, and a haircut for Tony as well as a Mother's Day greeting that I will not forget pasted on my bathroom mirror. If nothing else, this ordeal has helped me to truly appreciate the simple things we sometimes overlook in our busy lives.

While in Miami, I got to spend time with my family just laughing and talking and eating. Oh yes, I did get to see the movie Prom *with my sisters and nieces. It brought* back memories of high school days and a smile to my face when I looked down the row to see five ladies I love so much.

Was also able to visit Mom and Dad's church and meet some of the Miami prayer warriors who have been sending prayers up for me. I am so grateful and quite often speechless at the outpouring of support I receive. (That does not happen very often!)

We even experienced a "drive-through one-minute prayer" offered by some ladies on the side of the road. I don't think any of us have ever experienced prayer like it, but I guess prayer is prayer.

I also learned about a new supplement guaranteed to tackle any health issues and build your immune system made of chicken and cow mucus. I will keep everyone posted on that … Not sure I'm up for it, but you never know!

May 22, 2011

This wonderful week ended on a high note. Tests on Thursday were uneventful, just more of what is becoming more routine than I would like to admit. More drinking stuff that tastes like flavored chalk, more sticking, more disrobing, more prodding … Most of my inhibitions are long gone, but at least I've met some wonderful people who help make this process much more bearable. Another plus is the free parking for showing my hospital bracelet. Ah, the perks!

The week was incredibly uplifting on a personal level thanks to a visit from my cousin, Father Martin, from Annapolis. We had wonderful conversations and a great time together. I even challenged him to nine holes of golf, using the word "challenged" loosely. After my score of twelve on the first hole, we lost the two golfers who had invited us to join their party. I also had to chase down a bold squirrel that stole my energy bar from the golf cart (or rather Martin chased him down). Guess that little stinker didn't realize how important it is that I have my nutrients.

The highlight of Martin's visit had to be a special dinner followed by Mass and a special blessing in our home. The spirit was definitely present! We had to say good-bye on Friday, and we finished off his stay with a visit to Cowboy Stadium and the Museum of Biblical Art, but not before receiving results from my Thursday tests.

That news: reductions in size in the previously noted nodules and lesions. Wow! I have not met with the doctor yet (that happens tomorrow), but the report gives nothing but good news, and it details a decrease in all the trouble areas noted before.

May 24, 2011

It's Tuesday, the day after treatment four and a visit with my doctor and team. As we expected to hear, things are going great! Everything in the report was good news; all the tumors are shrinking and show improvement.

We learned that this treatment schedule will continue at least until the end of the year as long as we continue to get good results. Also, that I'll have to maintain some type of treatment plan for many years to come, *that I'll never be completely free from the threat of cancer, unless ... Unless science and our incredible medical researchers come up with a way to cure this disease, which I am going to do my part to help with. One way I'm going to help is by participating in the Susan G. Komen Three-Day Walk for the Cure with fourteen other incredible ladies who make up CC's Sisters.*

One of my favorite Bible verses is Romans 12:12: "Rejoice in hope, endure in affliction, persevere in prayer."

Thanks for helping me persevere!

July 24, 2011

I went through the second round of follow-up tests and scans on Thursday, checking my heart function and the various cancerous sites. It made for a long day, broken up by a lunch date with Jesse. (Not sure what I'd do if I didn't have the boys in my life.)

Someone asked if I'd had a good day. My reply was, "If you consider drinking about sixteen ounces of thick fluid, being poked with an IV, lying down and being run through a tube, and then having someone press really hard as they run a wand over your chest for thirty to forty-five minutes a good day, then I guess I had one."

Now the good point is that all of this was done in a wonderfully air-conditioned hospital when the temperature outside was about 102 degrees. Things could definitely be worse. And I did get a lunch with Jesse out of the deal.

I must admit, I'm not thrilled with the report, as I was all ready to put on my red tutu and do the happy dance. I was hoping to hear that the tumors had shrunk even more and that they were hardly distinguishable or that they'd completely disappeared. I was always a good student in school; I strive to be an over-achiever, and I've carried some of that into this battle.

The fact that I have a "good" report rather than a "stellar" report is somewhat disappointing, and I spent most of the weekend processing the reality of the situation. The reality is that I'm not always going to hit it out of the ballpark. I have to settle for a base hit at times and may even strike out some. I just want to end up winning this game. I have to become better at taking the not-so-good with the good and looking down the stretch while keeping myself in the game. I also need to remember the words of the doctor who told me this won't be a sprint but a marathon.

As I get ready for my next "at bat," I need to never underestimate the power of the fans and cheerleaders in the stands and along the sidelines. I also know I have to do a better job of turning it over to the One who is really in control.

To the many of you who are encouraging me along the way with special words, prayers, and actions, thank you so much. You are my Twelfth Man!

August 12, 2011

I am still busy training for the three-day walk. That's given me something to shoot for. Training comes early in the morning before the big heat, and we are working up to ten miles tomorrow. I love the walking;

it's something I feel I can still do well, unlike trying to remember which words to use in a presentation. Speaking of remembering, it was quite a relief to see the article in the newspaper about the reality of "Chemo Brain." Seems you <u>can</u> regain your mind after treatments, and boy is that something I look forward to!

I've had so many people offer words of support, and quite often I'm asked how I maintain a good attitude. So here it goes … I'm blessed to have a wonderful family and group of friends. They don't let me get down, or at least not for long. If I mention a disappointment or express negativity, I'm sure to be whipped back into shape by a phone call, text, or visit. Sometimes I'm not even sure how the message gets out before the reserves are being called in. (You know who you are!)

And living with all boys helps. There are no weenies allowed in our house, not even one of those little party weenies. All three of them help me stay on track but are quick to offer hugs and "I love yous" when needed.

And my faith … I guess I should have listed that first. My parents shared their faith with me my entire life, and though at times I probably fought them on it, I'm glad they persisted. That faith has taken center stage in my life now, and I don't know how I could manage without it. Just knowing I can be still and turn my worries over to God is such a relief. I have experienced miracles in this journey, some small and some really big. I happen to believe I'm living one now.

September 12, 2011

As a friend and I were visiting through my treatment, we discussed how someone lives normally, knowing they have Stage IV metastatic breast cancer. It made me stop and think.

I've lived nine months with this knowledge. Initially, I was overwhelmed with the thought of how much time I might be given. Then, as tomorrow came, I began to look to the future and realize that I needed to make the most of every day.

Things that used to be important suddenly seem silly in the big scheme of things. Not that I still don't get caught up with how my hair might look or if my outfit is in style, but hopefully I've put some of the important things in perspective.

I think that's what we should all remember, especially as we mark the tenth anniversary of the 9/11 terrorist attacks. No one is promised tomorrow; all we have is today. We need to take each day and live it the best we can.

I've been given the gift of time, a gift I pray I don't squander. "One day at a time." I know we hear these words all the time. In fact, we've probably said them ourselves many times, but how often do we really take them to heart?

When you realize that each day is truly a gift, you don't want to waste one minute on unpleasant tasks, people, or thoughts. That can sometimes be difficult, so please help me focus on good things ... Fun times with family and friends, positive experiences that really mean something, Florida football, one or two episodes of Dancing with the Stars, *and all the continued blessings I receive, rather than what I didn't get.*

September 29, 2011

A little rain in the forecast. You know how you don't really appreciate the rain unless you have so much sunshine that it gets old (or you live in Texas)? Or how God gives you trials and tribulations to prepare you for future blessings?

Well, I guess it's time for a little shower. After sailing through my first line of treatment for this dreadful disease, I've hit a bump. Although I still feel good, am still training for my walk in November, and am still convinced I'm going to kick this thing, my third set of scans showed a new area on one of my left ribs. Any new lesions of a certain size mean I have to drop out of the clinical study and look for alternate treatments. Unfortunately, my regular doctor was out of town and the doctor filling in had to deliver this news last Friday. To make sure the findings were accurate, I had an MRI the first of the week with a follow-up visit today to go over the results. The results stand, so it's time to bring in another cancer-fighting line-up!

I was lucky to have my support team with me for this visit — Joe, Ellie, and my sister Debbie, who flew in from Miami and Houston to be here. Although the news is not what I wanted, I am still optimistic that an effective treatment is out there. As the doctor said, it's still early in the game, and there are many options available. We just need to find the best weapon, and right now I'm very interested in beginning another clinical study.

I will meet with my regular doctor on Tuesday to see how we might go forward. In the meantime, I'll have an infusion tomorrow of Herceptin (a drug that has success with breast cancer), a bone scan on Monday, and then meet with Dr. Haley on Tuesday. We're investigating all the alternatives. I now know it's possible to live a good life while being treated, and that's what I intend to do. I also intend to continue doing whatever I can to over-come this disease, both for myself and for others. When I had the privilege of participating in Sing for the Cure as a narrator, there was always one piece that got a huge reaction, "Livin' Out Loud Blues." And that's what I'll be doing, livin' out loud!

That out loud livin' will start on Saturday night as we raise money for our three-day walk at our friend's art gallery in Lewisville. We have so many of the team here to celebrate our last major push for support, four from out of town and many others who have continued to support me through these last few months. That's what keeps me going ... The incredible love that surrounds me every day.

October 4, 2011

After a wonderful celebration on Saturday with friends and family raising money for CC's Sisters and Susan G. Komen, we are ready for round two.

I met with Dr. Haley today to review the latest, and I let her know she can't go out of town anymore. She confirmed what the scans have shown, that the cancer has resurfaced at a site on a rib and is in the bone. The good news is that she's managing another clinical study that involves some effective drugs; it's one I was looking at before we got into the most recent study I just finished. Several other doctors have recommended it as well, so we feel good about going forward with this next line of defense.

Dr. Haley explained to us that this will probably be our future ... Finding the right treatment for the moment, until it loses its effectiveness, and then it will be time for the next line of action. Joe compared it to a game of "Whack-a-Mole," where we'll be hitting it hard until that little stinker pops up somewhere else. We'll just have to keep changing the old mallet during this game.

Some of the positives of this whole craziness: they are always discovering new treatments, drugs, and so on; my body is healthy so I can take on this fight; the side effects of this treatment are minimal again; the medical professionals I interact with are awesome; I have the most incredible support base out there (if you're reading this, that means you); and God is good!

The downside: weekly infusions (scheduled for Tuesdays to avoid Manic Mondays); possibly some fatigue (and a few other discomforts); and no ice-cold beer with Florida football, or wine tastings with the gang, or margaritas with Mexican food.

All in all, I'm ready to start round two. Cancer doesn't know what it's up against. My goal is to play a part in finding a cure for this disease. Or a permanent treatment plan that allows people with cancer to live full lives without fear. I will do this!

Oh, and I'll still be able to do the walk with my wonderful group of "sisters." With only one treatment before the walk, there should be no problem with side effects. If you're looking for something to do the weekend of November 4–6, think about coming out and cheering us on! We'll be walking!

October 13, 2011

"Failure is only a temporary change in direction to set you straight for your next success."*

I'm not sure who said them, but I love these words. Although I've experienced a slight (temporary) failure, I'm ready for the next plan of action. It's just going to be delayed a little.

After completing one more test for my heart last week, my two boys and I headed to Miami to see family before I started my next round of treatments. It's always good to go home and visit the gang. We returned on Monday night, and I was ready for the "hook up" (no, not that kind). All reports came back good, and I was set to begin my new regimen of weekly infusions and daily pills. Dr. Haley assured me that I should handle this treatment well with some possible fatigue but no major concerns. She also said I should be able to get myself there and back without any problems, which is a relief, since getting someone to take me on a weekly basis could get challenging.

Settling in for "Happy Hour," I was connected and getting comfortable in the chair (which is quite a feat because those chairs are anything but comfortable) and started drifting off for a quick snooze. That's when the news came that I would have to wait for the magic potion. Apparently, the study calls for a three-week break from Herceptin (which I was given when my doctor was out of town), so I have to wait two weeks before starting the new treatment. This means I'm in a holding pattern until Tuesday, October 25. I'm getting a little antsy, but it will just be a little delay until show time. At least I'll have more than a week to shake off any side effects before the big walk.

Am praying the Serenity Prayer…"God grant me the serenity to accept the things I cannot change, the courage to change the things I can, and the wisdom to know the difference."

November 9, 2011

Two weeks ago I started my new treatment, another clinical study with the tried and true Herceptin and another one that has proven effective, vinorelbine. Another drug, everolimus, is to be added to the mix, and I have a 50/50 chance of receiving it.

I was concerned that the new treatment might prevent me from taking part in the three-day walk, but *that didn't happen! I was able to participate, along with fourteen other amazing women on our team (plus another three thousand), and we completed sixty miles in three days to raise money for breast cancer research. What a walk it was! CC's Sisters raised over $68,000!*

We started by leaving our homes at 6:00 a.m. on Friday morning to kick off the walk with opening ceremonies. I was honored to carry in the "Hope" flag and place it above the crowd in center stage. Standing in the middle of a sea of pink was more than I could handle, and tears starting rolling down my face. Looking out and seeing our team in the crowd was so moving, and then looking out and seeing my husband in the mass of spectators was overwhelming. As a survivor and flag bearer, I was among a group of eight who led the walkers out of the gate. I figured CC's Sisters would be leading the pack on the first day, but I was wrong.

I watched all the walkers go by, and finally my crew of beautiful women came around the bend. Apparently, they were caught in the back and had to make a potty stop. When I saw their smiling faces coming towards me, I was ready to go, and walk we did!

I can't express the emotions I felt. The people cheering along the way, the people walking alongside me, the love I felt for my teammates who have chosen to endure this challenge, Ellie's in-laws (or in-loves), who met us at lunch and made sure we had what we needed or didn't need as we shed our clothing along the way ... It was a very incredible experience.

Did I mention that the morning started with temperatures in the high thirties? Seeing all of our peeps and my family, especially my three boys, at cheering stations along the way helped re-energize our feet and spirits throughout the weekend.

The overnight accommodations were pretty basic. Two-man pink tents set up side-by-side on the grounds of Brookhaven College, meals served in a mess tent, showers in semi-trailers with outside sinks alongside the trucks, port-a-potties for doing your daily duty (or doody). But they did flush, or at least some of them did. Setting up our individual campsites, blowing up air mattresses, and organizing our stuff was an adventure in itself, especially since, with the exception of Amy, there aren't many experienced campers in our group.

The walking was incredible. Did our feet hurt? Were our legs sore? Did we rub blisters? Were we hungry for a lunch other than turkey/ham and cheese? You bet. But oh, what a weekend. To all of you who came out to cheer us on, thank you, thank you, thank you! My sister Ellie says it will take a while to adjust to not being cheered by just walking out the front door.

So many stories came out of this weekend ... Some we heard firsthand, some we learned through the signs posted along the way or worn on the backs of walkers. You realize how devastating this disease is, not just breast cancer but all cancers. You see how people have been impacted, enough to raise more than $7.1 million by walking sixty miles in three days. I am honored to be part of it.

November 30, 2011

The Thanksgiving holiday was wonderful, physically and mentally. My boys were all with me, along with my Ellie and her boys and her mother and father-in-law. We had a house on the ocean in Galveston and ate, slept, read, ate, walked, played cards and games, ate, read, watched football, ate ... It was wonderful. I came back invigorated and ready to go at it again.

I'm really looking forward to the Christmas holidays. This year, they're taking on special meaning. I have learned some wonderful things these last few months:

1. *To be careful when I hand brush the air and "pfft, pfft" something*

2. *That I am surrounded by awesome people*

3. *That a sixty-mile walk can be an incredible experience when surrounded by awesome people*

4. *There is no greater gift than love, but hope is definitely a close second*

5. *To be careful playing UNO® Blast® with the Elams*

6. *Or Beach Rummy (see previous note)*

7. *That "mucositis" is not a pretty word or condition, and no one deserves it (except for that lady in traffic)*

8. *That I truly am blessed!*

To all of you who sent birthday and get-well wishes, you made up for any discomfort I was feeling!

December 14, 2011

We received the results from a long day of testing and scans last week, and though it wasn't the news I was looking for, we are moving forward. I've learned there's always good and bad in everything, and that is so true when you're dealing with a chronic disease. The good news is that several of the trouble areas seem to be under control with no major progression, the mouth sores have retreated, and we still have treatments available to pursue. The bad news is that the area around my ribs and clavicle has progressed enough that I have to drop out of the most recent clinical study and start another treatment program.

After meeting with the doctor yesterday and additional conversations and research, I am still hopeful we will overcome this disease. There is so much work being done to find a cure; how can we lose? Just last week there was a conference in San Antonio focusing on breast cancer research, and each day new information comes out in the news. I'm proud to say that two of the treatments mentioned were studies I was involved in. What an incredible feeling to know I'm playing a small part in new medical developments!

January 10, 2012

The year is off to a big start for the Colangelos. We had a grand holiday in Dallas. Although we didn't travel to be with family in New York or Florida this year, we had Ellie, Drew, and IV here with us, along with special friends who are now family. It was wonderful to celebrate Christmas and the New Year without the worry of travel. And we will be traveling in the summer, as Joe has granted one of my bucket list wishes of a trip to Hawaii with all my boys.

On the medical front, we are looking forward to this year as being "our year." We have more weapons to pull out, and we are coming at this bothersome disease with all guns blazing. There are so many who have offered their help, support, and encouragement that it sometimes makes my head swim. As you know, making my head swim is like throwing flame accelerator on a smoldering fire. Keeping up with all the developments and discoveries in dealing with breast cancer is a full-time job in itself. I am becoming more educated in this area, more than I ever thought I would be, although retaining all that info is a challenge. If you see me, you'll probably notice that I take notes all the time, as evidenced by the note pads lying throughout my house. One of my biggest nightmares is getting somewhere without a piece of paper or a pen.

Here's where I am today: after the last scans that showed progression of the disease, I have started a new treatment plan that involves taking two drugs orally on a daily basis. The good thing about this is that my weekly visits to get an infusion aren't necessary at this time. Rather than sit in a chair for hours hooked up to a medicine drip, I simply pop a couple of pills with breakfast and dinner. Well, maybe more than a couple, and maybe a few even before I sit down for a meal. I remember teasing my parents about their "pill buffets" at mealtime ... Payback is hell!

I've also started daily radiation for three weeks to the trouble area. One thing I've learned is that the radiation not only targets the cells through the radiation stream but can also enhance the impact of the chemo, which is both good and bad news. Along with the good treatment and preventative effects of radiation, the side effects can be compounded. Although I've finally gotten rid of those horrible mouth sores, I feel more fatigue and stomach issues than previously. Each day is different, some with good energy and others somewhat impacted by runs to the bathroom. But in comparison to those who are confined to bed or limited by a disability, this is nothing.

I'll also be traveling to Baton Rouge this weekend for my first vaccine. As a friend, Bob, talks about the Power of Who, *I have definitely been blessed with whom. Through their friends, my incredible sister and brother-in-law learned of a doctor who has done extensive work in developing a vaccine in the treatment of this disease.*

As my sister says, "You're not going anywhere on my watch," and if you know Ellie, you know she means business. She and I took a road trip just after Christmas to meet with Dr. Elliot and learn more about his work. After reviewing my files and additional blood tests, he told us I'm a great candidate for this vaccine. Apparently, I have a great army in this battle but just lack the proper weaponry, so we are going to build up my weaponry to help with my immunity against this stupid cancer. I've also modified my diet and have included supplements that won't interact negatively with the treatments I'm getting.

Don't know what tomorrow will bring, but then, who does? I have learned to live each day for what it is, and if I can't take down and pack away my Christmas decorations all in one day, so be it. Normal tasks do take a little longer, given the rest breaks that are built in.

Each day is truly a gift, and I thank God each morning for giving me another one. I have experienced the loss of people without any advance notice and realize that none of us know what's coming next. I plan to get as much joy from each moment as possible, because there's so much to be joyful about. (As I type this, my sweet dog Maggie is curled up next to me.)

If I can be of help to anyone who is dealing with this stupid disease, I would love to help. My goal is to be part of the winning team that finally finds the cure for this crappy cancer.

February 1, 2012

By now, you've probably heard the outcry against Susan G. Komen for severing its relationship with Planned Parenthood. While the reasons for the dissolution differ depending on who is delivering the message (isn't that true of most any situation?), one thing that can't be argued is the role Susan G. Komen has played in the fight against breast cancer. I continually experience this organization's positive role in the progress being made to impact this disease.

As I previously mentioned, I was invited to participate in a roundtable with nine other women from around the country living with metastatic breast cancer. Not just breast cancer survivors but women who are still and probably always will suffer from this form of breast cancer for which there is no cure, just treatment. We were joined by about eight Komen staff who sat and listened to our stories. It was quite interesting, informative, and emotional.

Komen will be compiling the information and putting together an executive summary, but what came out immediately was the need to educate people about metastatic breast cancer and what it really means. Right now, we will never be able to say we are cured, which is quite different from the victorious picture of crossing the finish line. We can merely hope for time and quality of life in hopes that research will improve both for us.

I shared my involvement in the roundtable with my doctor and what it might mean for increased awareness of metastatic breast cancer. Her response was very positive, and she cited the role Komen has played in impacting breast cancer through the years. We just have a bigger monster to deal with now, and Komen is up for the task.

February 29, 2012

Wow, can't believe it's been a month. So much has happened. First of all, there's been a lot of celebrating in our house with the Giant's Super Bowl win! We were able to celebrate with my wonderful Uncle Leo and Aunt Sue and sister Anne (not a nun) as well as other friends who made the game a little more special.

While here, my Aunt Sue was a trooper in helping Joe administer my second vaccine … Actually, she administered, and Joe let me squeeze his hand. We administered my third vaccine just last night. This time, Joe administered and Tony (with a towel over his head so he didn't have to look) let me squeeze. So, three vaccines down, and hopefully the potion is building up my army! And I believe it is!

I was able to see Tony and his choral group perform a couple of weeks ago in San Antonio, and they were awesome. It was such an incredible experience to see those guys on stage and the audience jump to its feet with a standing ovation. I couldn't help but cry, along with the other parents and teachers. I want to see so many more performances like that.

I also travelled to Houston to present to Coldwell Banker United Realtors as they kick off their Making Strides Against Breast Cancer campaign. They invited me to speak to their office managers and ambassadors as they begin their fundraising efforts for the American Cancer Society's breast cancer fund. With Ellie and

Jesse there for support, I was able to share my story and encourage their group to fund breast cancer research as well as encourage participation in clinical trial studies. It was a very moving experience, and I am encouraged when I see so many people who have taken up this cause.

After that came a weekend retreat with my wonderful husband who is my rock. Along with two other couples and special friends Jamie and Sara and Rene and Laura, we spent a couple of days in the woods reflecting on our relationships and the part that God plays in our lives. This was an incredible experience, and I recommend it to anyone who treasures their marriage and family. It is so good for the soul, and this is such an important part of my treatment.

To finish off the month, I headed to Miami, where I joined Ellie and my beautiful nieces Abby and Becky in surprising my sister Debbie for a belated fiftieth birthday celebration. We also helped my parents get situated back in their condo after new floors were put in. Although there was plenty of work involved, when you do it alongside people you love, it just seems like fun. Now, if I can only convince the rest of them how fun it was (especially those who had to replace several toilets, Victor and Ellie). We were able to celebrate with a wonderful dinner along with all my family (minus my sister Anne, not the nun). It was a great visit, and I leave a piece of my heart behind every time I return home to Texas. I also had a short visit to Debbie's office, where I got to meet some of my support team and prayer warriors, people who, through their love and respect for my sister, have extended that love to me.

It's been an eventful month, full of hope and love. I'm excited to be attending the Susan G. Komen conference in Fort Worth at the end of this week and hopefully will hear how much closer we are to defeating this disease. I am completely committed to doing whatever I can to help those who have breast cancer as well as those who are doing what they can to find a cure or more effective treatments. As my hero Randy Jackson would say, "I am in it to win it!" (Randy Jackson is actually not my hero, but I love that line.)

March 5, 2012

Now for the great news! I had the honor of attending the Komen conference on Saturday, where I reunited with some of the awesome women who participated in the roundtable on metastatic breast cancer. I also attended a survivor's breakfast where I was able to sit at the table with founder and chair Nancy Brinker, global ambassador Tina Lewis, and Dr. George W. Sledge. Dr. Sledge is well known for his work with breast cancer and is the co-director of the breast cancer program at the Melvin and Bren Simon Cancer Center at Indiana University. It was an awesome experience, and I wish everyone could have heard the message that was delivered.

I believe we are winning this battle. The work being done through research and clinical studies is making an impact. When you look at the work in the last thirty years and what a breast cancer diagnosis meant then compared to what it means today, the change is incredible. Dr.

Sledge talked about all the progress being made and specifically discussed the HER2 type of cancer I have. He mentioned the explosion of drugs targeting HER2 and said he believes that in the next five years, we'll be talking about long-term survivors. Okay, so now the tears are streaming down my face! The theme was definitely the importance of research and clinical studies. We are where we are today because of it, and it doesn't happen by accident.

But did you know that only 3% of cancer patients choose to participate in clinical studies? Mention was made of the fear that dollars for research will drop because of the Komen controversy. Komen is one of the biggest contributors to research. In 2011 alone, the organization contributed $63 million, and since 1982, $685 million. If you check that against some of the other organizations that contribute to research, I think you will be surprised at their level of commitment. The doctors and professionals who spoke were no lightweights; one was the director of the Breast Oncology Center at the Dana Farber Cancer Institute and a professor of medicine at Harvard Medical School.

For my part, I will continue to do what I can to raise awareness of the need for research and to seek out clinical studies. I hope you will, too. I think I've finally realized what my mission in life is. Hearing about women years ago who were "scraped to the bone" when they underwent breast surgery and how that has changed makes me so hopeful for the future. When I meet some of these women who are surviving every day, I am amazed by the grace and light they project. It helps me realize what is really important and how silly this world of politics can be.

I've said that I don't want breast cancer to define me, and I don't. I don't want it to define anyone! The only way to achieve that is to find the cure, or at least effective treatments that allow women to live better lives.

As if you couldn't figure it out, I will be participating again in the three-day walk in November, the week before my niece's wedding in New York. Hopefully my feet will hold out. We are looking for others to join CC's Sisters or support our cause. You can learn more by visiting www.the3day.org if you're interested.

March 14, 2012

Okay, quick update. Had a doctor's appointment before my Herceptin drip today. We discussed my participation in the three-day walk in November, and there is some concern that I may not be able to complete the whole thing. It seems like friction exacerbates the foot problem I'm having. I assured my doctor that I'll listen to my body and only do what I can. You never know; by then I may be on another treatment that doesn't impact the feet like this one does. I just may borrow Tony's scooter if it gets to be too much. I could be the "Scooting Sister."

Our team is coming together again, and I'm pulling together some opportunities to raise money as well as awareness for this so-important cause. I would love to go a month without hearing of someone else who has been stricken with cancer. Until that happens, I'm going to be plugging away, doing what I can to make things better. You may get tired of hearing about it, but it's a message that needs to be heard. So for Debbie (not the sister), Netty, Drew (not the brother-in-law), Catherine, and so many others who are fighting the fight, I won't shut up. Not that anyone has ever been able to keep me quiet for long!

March 26, 2012

Do you know how much I hate this disease?

I said it; I hate it. I want you to hate it too, enough so that we do everything we can to find a cure, or at least a treatment that doesn't cause people pain and discomfort, whether it's physical or mental.

I hate this disease! Every time I hear of someone who has been diagnosed, whether it's a close friend or just an acquaintance, I hate it more! We may not talk much about it, trying to focus on the positive, but the reality is that it takes something from every one of us. Whether it's a sense of security, a little bit of confidence, or a breast, it takes something. And it takes work and love to overcome that loss.

God bless the people who work every day to make a difference in the lives of those who have been affected, whether it's the doctors treating their patients and struggling to find the right plan for each individual; the researchers trying day in and day out to discover how to outwit the incredibly tricky and continuously morphing cells; the nurses who greet their patients each day with their personal magic potion and compassion;

the volunteers who give their time and energy to improve the lives of those who have been touched; or the cancer veterans who celebrate those who have won the battle, cheer those who are still fighting, and do what they can to improve the lives of their sisters.

I hate this disease! But hopefully I can continue to look through the hate and recognize the love and beauty that in better days may have been hidden or overlooked. This beautiful time of year just reminds me that to whom much has been given, much is expected. Without the rain, there would be no rainbows. So I will continue to fight and spread the message about the need for research and hope.

I hate this disease! But I love this life!

May 27, 2012

It's Memorial Day weekend. This may not be one of the biggies as far as holidays go, but it's always a special day for me. I love putting on that patriotic music, thinking about those who have given so much for us, and enjoying a three-day weekend with my family, prepping for summer and waiting for school to end.

I'm beginning to train for the big walk in November and will do the best I can. Feeling great this morning, I took sweet Maggie on a long walk. The weather is still somewhat cooler then, and it was a beautiful, sunshiny, breezy morning. As I walked, I had my music on, and it always seems to speak to me, delivering timely messages that help me stay in perspective.

My walks are a good way to reflect, and I do think God has a way of whispering messages to me. That's why I miss them so much when I'm not feeling up to going out. Today, I thought about a wonderful wedding I went to on Friday evening, the marriage of the son of some great friends. A lot of our friends were there, and we had a great time catching up and sharing the love.

Among the guests was a gentleman who is fighting stage IV cancer. Like me, he's going through chemo and experiencing similar side effects. What was so cool was the smile on his face and how he joined in the celebration on the dance floor. His spirit and attitude were awesome, and at the end of the evening, we shared our thoughts. We are not guaranteed tomorrow – none of us are – so we need to wring every bit of happiness and joy out of each moment handed to us.

I have said something before that I must correct. I have said that cancer has been a blessing to me, and that's wrong. A blessing is something I wish for others, and I would not wish cancer on anyone, not even that person who cuts me off in traffic. But from cancer, many blessings have flowed.

Cancer reshapes your thinking. It causes you to step back and ask yourself questions, such as "Is that really important?" and "Is that really worth the aggravation?" and "Is the fact that my toes aren't polished or my face doesn't have that stylish sun-kissed glow really worth the worry?"

The answer I come up with most often (though sometimes I have to do some self-talking) is "No!" The *biggest blessing is realizing that we need to live each day doing what is truly important and enjoying what has been given to us: the people we love, the beauty of nature that surrounds us, and the gifts we've been blessed with (and I don't mean the material ones). Although I don't get up every day singing, I might just try to hum.*

As the breeze was blowing today, I thought about my faith. I do believe that God is in our lives, and I'm sure some who are reading this doubt it. But walking through the wind and watching what it does to the trees and leaves, feeling it on my face, I realize that it too is something we never see. Some days we can feel it more than others, but no one questions that wind exists.

That's how it is for me in the faith department. I know God is there, and some days I feel His presence more than others. That faith is what keeps me going!

July 2, 2012

This past year, many people have shared their thoughts with me through this blog or in other conversations, and some have called me an inspiration. I learned when I was young that you shouldn't let things go to your head, so I've been uncomfortable with those words. I recognize that any inspiration comes from God and the special people who have impacted my life. The world lost one of those people on Sunday.

Mom Colangelo, my husband's mother, passed away after a decline in her health that couldn't be overcome. Through her eighty-seven years, she was the picture of grace, light, and joy. I thought she was beautiful, not in the way magazines and pop culture portray beauty but beautiful in the way she lived her life. She looked like a grandma. She didn't dress so that she appeared younger than she was; she didn't apply makeup or use techniques to cover up the wrinkles she'd earned; she cared about looking like who she was – Marie Colangelo, mother, grandmother, great-grandmother.

When describing her, I often think of The Andy Griffith Show. *Remember Aunt Bea? Well, that's how I saw my mother-in-law. Sweet, caring, always worrying about others, and always making sure you had something to eat.*

Marie was the foundation of her family. She stayed current on what was happening in the world and around her and welcomed discussion. She wasn't afraid of sharing her opinion, but she always shared it in a nonthreatening way, without the crude and polarizing language that is so often used today. She loved everyone ... Her family and friends, friends of friends, and friends of friends of friends! But especially her grandchildren and her newest great-granddaughter.

When I had the privilege of joining the Colangelo clan seventeen years ago, she welcomed a new older grandchild, Jesse, with open arms. Although the Colangelo blood doesn't run through his veins, the Colangelo love runs through his heart. Always afraid of showing favoritism to one of her brood, she would often mention all her wonderful children (and their spouses) if she had just

72

praised another, making sure everyone felt their value. She wanted to be sure everyone knew they were loved.

Her faith in God was great and unwavering and a true inspiration to me. Although the Texas branch of the family wasn't able to enjoy her company as regularly as those who lived near her, we had the chance to experience special times when we called or visited. Most times, we stayed with her. They weren't the typical accommodations you might expect when you talk about a trip to New York, but they were some of the most welcoming accommodations you will ever find.

Most of our time was spent around her dining room table. I will miss those conversations most of all. There, if something was troubling you, you were comforted. If you had doubts, they were resolved. If you needed encouragement, you got it. Her pearls of wisdom helped guide you through difficult times. And no matter what she did or said, she did it with love. At her core was her faith in God. She often said, "Leave it in God's hands," and she did. Even when she lost her partner and the love of her life, she never questioned God's love. She grieved, but she continued honoring God.

Today our family is grieving the loss of a wonderful lady and the cornerstone of our family. But as she would say, we'll leave her in God's hands and remember the words from the Bible: "Well done, good and faithful servant." This week, as others celebrate our great country, we will be celebrating an inspirational woman who helped make our country great!

August 3, 2012

It's been a month since my last post, and so much has happened. I can't believe that just one month ago we were celebrating the life of an incredible woman, my mother-in-law. Joe and I travelled to New York to attend two funerals, one for Mom Colangelo and one for her brother, Anthony Maida, who joined Mom just four hours after she left this life. It was an emotional few days, but we were able to share them with family and friends who held all of us up with love.

Just five days after returning from New York, my three boys and I hopped a plane to a dream vacation in Hawaii. Yep, check that one off the old bucket list. Mom and Dad travelled down in first class while we let the boys slum it in coach. It was a great start to a great ten days. The first five days we spent at Waikiki Beach, with the remainder spent on the island of Maui.

We had a great time! It was just what we needed to revive our spirits. We were also able to meet up with Ellie and her family along with other friends in Maui. The weather was great, the temperature cooler than Texas, and God's beauty surrounded us in so many ways.

My feet held up, and I was able to climb to the top of Diamond Head. I climbed slower than I might have previously and made some stops along the way, but the reward at the top was breathtaking. Having my boys with me made it all the better.

So here's the medical update ... I am still taking the trial vaccine with no major bad side effects and my hands and feet are doing better, though some days are more uncomfortable than others. I have been sporting shoes quite regularly and have graduated to a "mini heel" on some occasions. Ah, simple pleasures.

I am training slowly for the three-day walk in November and am so hopeful that I will make all sixty miles with an incredible team surrounding me. Thinking of everything that has happened in the last month reminds me of how precious time is and all that is possible in just a small amount of time.

I definitely hope for years and years to enjoy all I have been given, but if my time is shortened, I hope I can continue to enjoy each day, each hour, each minute, as much as possible. My family and friends are surely helping me accomplish that, and I give thanks every day for that!

Much love and many blessings.

P.S. Please keep praying for a cure for cancer, of all kinds. It continues to impact the lives of so many people I love.

August 26, 2012

Update time ... The tests came back, and though they aren't what I was hoping for — cancer free — I'll take whatever good news I can get. Not much pain is involved, since I have this port they can access for all the other things they need to run through my body. If you can picture a car at a pump gassing up, that's what I often feel like when I'm receiving treatments.

So here's the news: kidneys show some suspicious areas that aren't consistent with simple cysts. In light of that and the fact that my father had renal cancer, I'm scheduled for an MRI in a week. More time in the tube, and a much more confining one at that, but at least an hour of "down time" is guaranteed.

I have lovingly begun to refer to the MRI tube as my "inspiration chamber," as I have come up with a number of speeches and great ideas as I'm being zapped. I also know that I'm never truly alone when I'm in there, and that gives me comfort.

The good news is that with the new treatment regimen, I will most likely be able to do the three-day walk in November. I was starting to worry because of my feet issues on the old drugs. This means I will be going full steam ahead on training once my feet are healed. One down side with one of the treatment options is that I'll probably lose my hair again. Although I've been there and done that and made the most of it, it's not really something I'm excited about going through again. Oh well. I'll just revive my scarves and get some new locks.

All in all, I feel good, am looking forward to cheering on my Gators this weekend in Gainesville, and will be preparing my next creative work in my inspiration chamber in about a week. To modify a quote from The Hunger Games, *"Let the games begin, and may the odds be ever in my favor!"*

September 7, 2012

I had the gift of about one hour of uninterrupted time yesterday in my inspiration chamber ... It was just me and my thoughts and a loud thumping noise as the machine did its job. Not sure of the results yet, but am expecting good news!

It gave me time to reflect on my recent visit to my old stomping grounds at the University of Florida, getting together with old friends and sharing (some of) my collegiate experience with Joe and Tony, only with a lot less beer and partying. The trip started when we landed in Jacksonville and had a day enjoying the Atlantic Ocean with a dear friend, from my early days, and her husband. As we boated to our lunch spot, dolphins jumped in our wake. Remember, dolphins mean good luck and long life!

We enjoyed dinner with an old college buddy and his wife and met up with my sister Debbie and her husband for a meal on the water in St. Augustine. Then on to the home of the Fighting Gators! It was a hot day for football, but that didn't dampen the spirits of the huge gang roaming the streets in preparation for the big game.

The tailgating parties have grown. Everywhere you looked was orange and blue and Gator apparel. I loved showing Joe and Tony around and pointing out landmarks. I shared the story of the tower and how every time a virgin graduates, a brick falls. (Didn't mention that the tower still has every original brick.) Then it was on to the president's suite, where we had the privilege of watching the game. We missed out on the crowd noise and excitement but also missed out on the extreme Gainesville heat! The Gators ended up winning (yeah!), and Tony made a couple of friends with the dean as well as the director of development in the college of liberal arts and sciences. I think I might have a future Gator in my family!

The weekend ended with a visit with a girlfriend from my junior high days whom I haven't seen in about sixteen years. We started talking about people in our lives and how important they are, and I reminded my friend that I'm like a boomerang. Once I meet you, I always come back. You never know when, but if I can find you, I'll try to reconnect. Joe calls it stalking. I call it, "Once in my life, always in my life."

As I wait for the results from this latest test, I know that whatever the outcome, I'll give thanks for the life I have, rich in friendships and the support of so many people around me.

Let's spread the wealth!

September 29, 2012

As a result of my latest treatment, I've started to shed my hair. As I learned in the past, it's best to take the bull by the horns, so rather than eating my meals with unwanted ingredients, leaving a trail of hair wherever I go, and wondering when the next big clump might choose to disengage, I scheduled a shave with Jeff, my favorite stylist and friend. I also volunteered to have the procedure filmed for an upcoming interview I'll be doing for television in the next few weeks.

Seemed like no big deal until the time got closer and I walked through the doors, but with Jesse there for support and Wally and Lauren (the cameraman and PR rep) by my side, along with the special stylists at the salon, we got down to business.

Actually, those clippers felt kind of good as the hair fell away. Once again, I discovered that the stinky old chemo actually causes your hair to gray (not that good years of living have anything to do with it) and that my ears stick out quite a bit more than I remembered. But in the end, it was just hair that will be replaced with scarves, hats, and at times a stylish little wig. And for the time being, my lint roller will be getting additional use as I give my head the occasional going over and pick up the little hairs I leave on my pillow, furniture, and clothes.

With Breast Cancer Awareness month approaching in October, I will be focusing on what I can do to help in this fight; raising money and awareness of the need for research and programs; trying to help others as they deal with life as a cancer fighter (or supporter); and enjoying the blessings I've been given from above and through the work of dedicated doctors, nurses, and researchers. I'm trying to remain humble in my fight, remembering, "When pride comes, then comes disgrace, but with humility comes wisdom" (Proverbs 11:2).

October 16, 2012

Gosh, time seems to be flying. I can't believe the big walk is in three weeks. Since we're old pros at it, the team isn't doing as many long training walks as last year. I'm just really excited to get out there with the sisters and do our thing.

I've completed two of the new treatments and have another four to six to go. After I finish this series, I'll remain on two of the three drugs for an indefinite time. The good news is that the drug we'll be eliminating from the potion is the "hair preventative," so my hair should come back. The fun is in seeing how it will come back — hopefully not all gray.

I had company at my last treatment, the TV camera, which accompanied me to film footage to be used for a live interview scheduled for tomorrow night on Fox 4 news. It was interesting watching the cameraman and reporter maneuver in the room with the nurse hooking me up to my special juices. The camera got pretty close to my face many times, and I just hope that HD TV is good to me. (God forgive me for all the times I've commented on how someone looks because of high definition.)

I also had the chance to speak at a local mall as part of the Breast Cancer Awareness activities. Yep, that was me talking as shoppers walked by, racing to their blue light specials. I remember times when I was out shopping while something similar was going on. I didn't always pause to listen. Well, some people do pause, and it was amazing to receive so much love after I stepped off the stage. Some people wanted to share their experiences, some wanted to say thanks, and one lost her mom last year to breast cancer and wanted a hug. I have said this before, but it was a most humbling experience.

I know that I sometimes question why I feel it's important to be so vocal and visible regarding breast cancer and my personal journey. It's not bringing me fortune and fame, although it does bring me attention. (Those who've known me through the years know I've never been afraid of attention.) I think I want people to know it can happen to anyone, it can happen more than once, and it's not glamorous. It's not a disease <u>she</u> might get; it's a disease <u>you</u> can get. It's not always a disease that will impact your life for a few months or a year; it can impact your life for a lifetime. It doesn't just affect you; it affects many people around you, especially your family. It's not always fun, but it is doable, with good times rolled in.

I think the real answer to why I do this came this past weekend. I was out shopping with Joe, and when I was looking at a shirt, the saleswoman came up to me and asked, "Does it hurt when you have breast cancer?" She caught me off guard, and then she added, "I heard that if it hurts, it's not cancer."

I'm always amazed at the people who recognize the "badge" — a bald head in a cap or scarf. Some glance away, some smile, and some reach out in some way to show support. This lady was looking for reassurance.

My response was that it could hurt, that one of my cancers did have pain. She went on to share that she had *a painful area in her breast but was afraid to go to the doctor. I told her, "Go and get it checked." We talked a little bit, and at the end of the conversation, she said she would.*

Whew. I've thought a lot about that and the people I've encouraged to get a check-up. Why are they fearful? It's either something or it's not. If it's not anything, getting it checked relieves the stress. If it is something, the sooner it's taken care of, the better the chances for a good outcome and full recovery.

If I can show people that life doesn't stop just because you have breast cancer, that there's still a lot of living to do, that you can overcome physical imperfections or blemishes with creative design, and that this world still holds a lot of beauty and opportunity, then I have served my purpose. So, I will continue to share the words of FDR: "The only thing we have to fear is fear itself."

Or perhaps the words of Joe's hero, Larry the Cable Guy, "Git 'er done!"

October 21, 2012

Yesterday was the first of the two events Komen is sponsoring in Dallas to raise money to impact the fight against breast cancer. This was the Komen Dallas Race for the Cure (5K). It can get confusing, but this event was put on by the Dallas affiliate, and 75% of the money raised goes to local programs here in the Dallas area, sponsoring mammograms and diagnostic services and helping the uninsured and underserved get the medical help they need. The other 25% goes for research.

The three-day walk in a couple of weeks is a national event held in about fourteen cities across the U.S., with 75% of the money going to research and 25% going to local programs. All of it is important, but what has impacted my life the most is the research part. Luckily, I'm blessed with insurance coverage to help with a good part of the costs.

Whatever anyone thinks about the Komen controversy, let me (hopefully) non-politicize it and share with you why their work, and the work of so many wonderful organizations, is so important.

Jesse and I were invited to do a live interview Friday morning for the local television station Fox 4, the media sponsor for the 5K. It was an early and cold morning, not quite fifty degrees, when we arrived. (I know my friends up north might be snickering to read the word "cold" to describe fifty degrees, but remember, I'm Miami-born and a Texas resident now.) We shared a snippet of my battle with cancer, and then Jesse shared some of his feelings and the reasons he put together a team for the walk. Not expecting that many would see it early on a Friday morning, and recording it so that we'd have proof that we really were on television, we chalked it up as being our five seconds of fame.

We joined up the next morning, Jesse and about twenty of his friends, one of my sweet, sweet friends and her beautiful daughter, and me. We got off to a late start, bringing up the rear of the group of about 20,000-plus walkers participating in the 5K. As Jesse shared with me, coordinating his group was a feat in and of itself!

We stopped for some photos, and this is where the "aha" moment occurred. A lady about my age called out to Jesse and told him she recognized him from the interview the previous morning. She wanted a picture with him because our interview was the reason she'd signed up to participate.

In my efforts to convey why it's so important that we continue to fight this battle, I've shared that I often question my motivation and expectations. Why do I worry so much that people hear my story, that they realize how important research is, that they understand why I choose to overlook the missteps that a great organization has made to look at all the good they do?

I do this so that one day my children and their partners, my nieces and goddaughters and their families, my friends and friends of friends, all my beloved sisters, might be saved from this disease. And if it's not this disease, that the research done in breast cancer's name may cross over to overcome the debilitating disease they are fighting.

I do it so that maybe my message will motivate one more person to get involved, or maybe to get that test they've been dreading. So that maybe their words will cause someone else to take positive action to make a change. So that maybe their action will be the tipping point that makes a difference. You know, that old ripple or butterfly effect, where one small action has a larger impact down the road as the initial action interacts with other factors in its path.

Maybe the action by someone who heard the message might bring that needed dollar to fund the life-changing research necessary to conquer a disease that has conquered so many beautiful women, men, and children. Maybe someone formerly undecided about where they want to concentrate their work might decide to become the researcher who finally unlocks the secret to this disease. Maybe one more person might decide to do what they can to make a difference.

To all those who got up yesterday to walk or run about three miles, to all those who plan on walking sixty miles in three days in the upcoming weeks, to those who have donated their time or money to help sponsor one of the participants, and to the very special group of twenty-somethings who made a walk through North Dallas a fun adventure (especially team captain Jesse), I say thank you for starting that ripple.

In the words of Edward Everett Hale (some attribute similar words to Helen Keller), "I am only one, but I am one. I cannot do everything, but I can do something. And because I cannot do everything, I will not refuse to do the something that I can do. What I can do, I should do. And what I should do, by the grace of God, I will do."

Thank you, God, for giving me the ability to do something!

November 13, 2012

The three-day walk was awesome. Where else can you walk with a special group of women amidst a larger group of 1,600; spend three days and sixty miles talking, laughing, complaining, aching, sweating, and loving;

and then want to sign up to do it again, all while raising more than $52,000?

Okay, I admit I took a small break on the second day and only did fifty-five miles. Although there weren't as many walkers this year, most of the cheering stations weren't quite as full, and the temps were much hotter than last year, it was well worth it. Special thanks to special friends Paula and Greg and Coby and Marcy and Dylan for pulling together the most awesome cheering station at Pokes in Addison. And for everyone else who turned out to support us, the love was flowing!

Although there were some minor mishaps, nothing major happened. I am proud to say the CC's Sisters did their part to make a difference. As Mother Teresa said, "We can do no great things, only small things with great love," and we did our small thing with a lot of love. And we celebrated!

After a few days for recovery and medical tests, we headed off to New York for another celebration, the marriage of our niece Jennifer to Bill, who is joining Joe's side of the family. It was a fabulous wedding and wonderful to be among all the Colangelos, eating and drinking and eating again ... It's always hard to leave because so much life happens in between visits, life that I definitely don't want to miss out on.

But we are back, and it's time to plan for the next celebrations ... Thanksgiving, Christmas, New Year's. I love this time of year and wish I could hold on to each moment a little bit longer.

I head to the hospital on Thursday for the fourth treatment of, hopefully, just a series of six. So far it seems like things are going well ... Soon I should have the results of the scans we took last week so that we have a better idea of what's going on. Maybe I can put on that little red celebratory dress that has been hanging in my closet just waiting to come out and show its stuff. God knows I love a celebration!

November 19, 2012

One of my favorite Bible verses is this: "To every thing there is a season, and a time to every purpose under heaven: a time to be born, and a time to die; a time to plant, and a time to pluck up that which is planted; a time to kill, and a time to heal; a time to break down, and a time to build up; a time to weep, and a time to laugh, a time to mourn, and a time to dance ..." (Ecclesiastes 3:1–4).

It seems like we've experienced all of that in one week (with the exception of "a time to kill," although I've received a few looks that could kill for things I've said). This verse continues to remind me that we never know what plans are in store for us.

Returning from the celebration in New York, we settled back into our reality here, which meant a trip to the doctor to review my scans and get my fourth treatment. But this time, the news was not the "red dress celebration" kind but another little bump in the journey. While the scans show that the stomach is clear (yeah!), the liver and kidneys are clear (yeah!), and the bones are clear (yeah!), the tumor in my lungs has grown. The fourth treatment of this series was cancelled and we decided to go forward with another drug, eribulin, which I will receive along with the Herceptin.

I'll share that this kind of threw me for a loop. Having functional hands and feet, feeling good, walking sixty miles (okay, fifty-five), and not really experiencing any discomfort that one might expect when fighting cancer lulled me into thinking I have this thing beat, even though I look like Kojak with my bald head.

When you get news that it might not be going as well as you think, you take a step back and some of the fears resurface. It takes time to get the mojo back. Luckily, Ellie was here for this visit, and afterwards we got some great comfort mac and cheese from Al Biernat's. Then I retreated to bed for the evening.

So the rollercoaster continues ... A dip in the ride on Thursday, a high point on Saturday to celebrate my birthday with my incredible boys, another dip on Sunday when I learned that my Uncle Red passed away, and so it goes.

I am reminded of the theme song from **The Lion King:** *"It's the Circle of Life, and it moves us all, through despair and hope, through faith and love, till we find our place, on the path unwinding, in the Circle, the Circle of Life."*

December 15, 2012

As I sit in the waiting room with my fellow combatants who are fighting to stay alive, we listen to the reporters on television detailing the horrific details of the gunman who in a matter of minutes took so many lives at an East Coast elementary school. I look around the room and see those who join me each week, coming regularly in hopes of receiving that magic elixir that will give them more years in which to enjoy their blessings. It hits me, how strange life can be. Here is a room full of people doing everything they can to stay alive, while at the same time someone deliberately snuffs out other people's lives. It doesn't make sense to me, and hopefully it doesn't make sense to you either.

I have been blessed with this life, no matter what it entails, and I plan on using it to do whatever I can to make a difference to those around me and to enjoy every bit of living there is. I assure you, it's not always easy, and I have to make many adaptations and modifications from week to week, day to day, and often minute to minute. But as I often say, "In the big scheme of things, it's not so bad."

As I think about those parents who will never again hug their children, about the childhood dreams that will never be realized, it puts into perspective my trivial worries about applying mascara to my one or two remaining eyelashes and minimizes the fact that for several hours each week, my daily routine is interrupted by a trip to the hospital to receive a drug that will play games with my body.

What I will remember is that I am so thankful I live in an age with treatments that give me extra days in which to enjoy my family, friends, and amazing surroundings. That there are so many devoted people who put their lives on the line daily in so many ways to protect my life (and yours) and ensure that I have those extra days to enjoy. That the world is full of wonderful nurses and doctors who work so hard to make sure a diagnosis doesn't mean you have to stop living. That I have been blessed with so many people who make me want to take every bit of living there is and glorify God who has given me this gift. I still believe that those who value this wonderful life far outnumber those who don't.

Now, go out and hug your kid, mother, father, husband, wife, sister, brother, friend, or a stranger. Give thanks for this wonderful life you have been given! And remember John 3:16: "For God so loved the world, that He gave His only begotten Son, that whoever believes in Him shall not perish, but have eternal life."

Merry Christmas!

In spite of Cindy's gratitude and perspective, the cancer was irrevocably on the move, and this would be her last Christmas with her family. Not surprisingly, she faced the coming months with grace and dignity, her family and friends firmly by her side, and her faith and courage in full force.

Chapter Three

FAMILY, FRIENDS, AND FAITH IN ACTION

"She learned from everything. She got knocked down, but she wouldn't stay down."

—Ellen Elam

*A*s Cindy's battle with cancer intensified, her family helped her check off as much as possible from her personal bucket list. They weren't giving up, but they were determined to live as fully as possible whatever time they had.

Cindy traveled extensively around Texas and to New York and Miami to attend family gatherings, reunions with old friends, Tony's school events and musical performances, and football games. She refused to miss one special moment.

In recalling all the family milestones his mom was determined to attend, Jesse marveled, "Everyone would have understood if she couldn't make it, but she had to be there every time."

In the end, it was the mundane, daily routines that Cindy cherished the most, like lunches or lounging around on Sunday afternoons with "my boys." Twenty-six-year-old Jesse was now working as a project manager for his father's company (custom flooring) while pursuing his love of music as a DJ at local night spots, and fifteen-year-old Tony was busy with soccer, playing trumpet in the high school band, and setting his sights on his learner's permit.

Together, Joe, Jesse, Tony, and Ellen worked hard to make sure that Cindy was as comfortable as possible and that she could be as active as possible for as long as possible. They knew she wanted to live and love every moment.

"We would be doting on her, and she would have a weak moment where she would start to feel like a burden," Joe recalled. "But then she would stop and say, 'I'm not going to be a whiny butt.' We wanted to be there for her, but as I've said before, she was really our rock."

Cindy was inundated with messages from family, friends, and even strangers who sent notes of support and prayers. Invariably, these notes talked about how Cindy had impacted their lives and inspired them. Even when Cindy had never met these people, she treated them like friends. Of course, no one was really a stranger to Cindy.

Following are a few additional examples of her faith in action and how much she enjoyed and appreciated living and loving her family and friends even in her final months in the arena.

January 4, 2013

A year of hope ... And when I say hope, I don't mean a "close your eyes and cross your fingers" type of hope. Not the kind of hope you had when you were a kid, hoping you would make the team. Or that of a teenager hoping that someone special would call (or these days text) to ask you out. Or the kind of hope we have as adults when the television announcer calls out the winning numbers for the Mega Lotto drawing. I'm talking about the hope we hold in our hearts, trusting that the challenges we face will evolve into something easier to manage or even be completely resolved. A hope that is marked by a belief that there is something much greater than any one of us and a knowledge that brings us peace, knowing all will be well.

This is my year of hope. It's now been two years since I was told the disease had spread, that there is no cure, that the best hope is to slow down or hopefully stop the progression. And here I am. Since I'm not looking at statistics (as directed by one of my awesome doctors), I'm not sure where I stand in regard to beating them. Well, maybe I did peek at a couple, but I didn't like what I saw so I just ignored them and moved on. I plan on this being my best year yet!

I've adjusted to the fact that there is no real normal anymore. For a while, normal might be a trip to the hospital for treatment once a week for two weeks, with a third week off for good behavior (well, not really good behavior, but at least a break), or maybe no hair but good use of my hands and feet. Then normal might change without much notice. I might get hair back but experience painful feet and be unable to use my hands, as happened this summer. Or normal might mean that I experience no real side effects and live among other normal people for a while.

There's a little ditty sung by Frank Sinatra that I love and have been known to sing to help turn things around:

Next time you're found, with your chin on the ground,

There's a lot to be learned, so look around.

Just what makes that little old ant

Think he'll move that rubber tree plant?

Anyone knows an ant, can't

Move a rubber tree plant.

But he's got high hopes, he's got high hopes,

He's got high apple pie, in the sky hopes.

So any time you're gettin' low

'Stead of lettin' go, just remember that ant ...

Oops, there goes another rubber tree plant.

(Frank Sinatra lyrics are property and copyright of Universal Music Group.)

  The thing is, we can't just sit back hoping; we have to take action. That's what I'll be doing in 2013, taking action to make sure 2013 will be my best year yet. I have a couple of projects I'm working on ... Compiling stories so I can write a book with my father about my grandfather's old-fashioned drugstore in Miami (Allen's Drugstore), putting together a plan for those who have been blessed with physical differences, and helping to spread words of encouragement to others. I'm gonna be like that little old ant Frank sings about.

  When I'm not relying on the wise words of Ol' Blue Eyes, I'll look to the Bible and remember what it says in Romans 15:13: "May the God of hope fill you with all joy and peace in believing, so that by the power of the Holy Spirit you may abound in hope."

  P.S. To all those who have sent encouraging words of support through the guestbook on this site or sent email messages or cards or made phone calls, you have no idea the value those have had in my life and the role you play in helping me stay on course. The love is overwhelming and is sent right back to you!

January 11, 2013

The final major holiday act is complete, and now it's time to really kick in to 2013. That act, taking down the Christmas tree, is always a melancholy one for me. Although I'm usually ready to put it up, organize, and clean, it means another year has passed.

I have found that taking down the tree is almost more memorable than putting it up. When putting it up, you're in that mad rush to make it Christmas, to make sure each ornament is put in the proper place, not giving much thought to the stories behind them. But taking down the tree, you aren't in quite the same hurry. Taking it down allows you time to stop and think and remember. Each ornament is special and has a story to tell, and so many involve new and old memories of friends and family.

This year, the newest addition to our collection was a cross given to me by a fellow youth leader at our church commemorating our attempt to share our faith with our youth and hopefully make a positive impact in their fragile lives. Time will tell.

I look at ornaments that a sister has given me ... the Irish shamrock, the glass hummingbird, the ornaments beautifully hand-painted on the inside (how do they do that?), the snow globe ornaments that reflect my fascination with snow globes dating back to watching the old

Shirley Temple movie Heidi *(Boys, please forget the year the movie interrupted a major football game between the Jets and Raiders), the special ornaments handmade by our young boys with love for their momma, the equally special handmade ornaments made by a special friend, representing the decorations that adorned her family tree many years ago ...*

The series of ornament frames that display our individual family photos, once used to mark our places at holiday celebration dinners with friends, now marking those memories on the tree ... Ornaments that are more than forty-five years old, made by a young boy and carefully preserved by his mother, to one day pass down to his wife and family ... Ornaments given by special people in our lives, years before those lives took the twists and turns that would become our lives today ... Tacky (some might say) representations of our favorite sports teams given by those (usually family) who understand our allegiance to the Gators, Yankees, Giants ... The variety of angels representing the many angels who have played a big part in our lives, some fragile and made of glass, some collector ceramic angels passed on by Mom, and some just simple angels ... Ornaments depicting Spiderman, Superman, Shaquille O'Neill, Batman, Tony the Tiger, the Simpsons, Barney, the Veggie Tales, Ninja Turtles, Mickey Mouse, the Grinch, all representing special times in the lives of growing boys.

Add in the ornaments we "won" in Christmas ornament exchange parties through the years. Maybe these weren't special ornaments at the time, but they do bring *back memories of good times. Other ornaments commemorating the first baby, the first year together, other firsts remembered years later, including a big bell given to me by a friend to represent my love of hand bell choirs (or not), a reminder of one more time I stuck my foot in my mouth and provided a funny story to tell. Ornaments spelling out glittery words expressing the feelings that guide our lives now, such as "Believe" and "Hope." The crooked angel at the top of the tree with broken wings, missing her left hand, her hair in disarray, who makes <u>our</u> tree our tree ...*

So many ornaments given to us by people who have been and remain a part of our lives ... It seems like our Christmas tree in December is a reflection of the memories we have made throughout the previous year and years. Maybe that's why taking it down is so special. It gives me time to think, remember, and reflect on good times gone by and look forward to those yet to come.

Would I ever give in to one of those beautiful, perfectly decorated Christmas trees that coordinate with the year's holiday décor?

I don't think so. My mismatched tree represents years of love, friendship, and life ... memories I wouldn't trade for anything, and memories I will continue to make in 2013!

January 31, 2013

There have been developments in my little journey. It seems like January is not a good month for me in the cancer department, and 2013 is keeping up the streak. I've been experiencing some discomfort from old "leftie," and I mentioned it to my doctor at my last visit. Although she couldn't feel anything, I went ahead and had a sonogram that showed a suspicious area, the same area that started all this trouble four years ago.

The results are in. I'm not happy with them, but they're not completely unexpected. It's cancer again. The positive in all this is that we're able to run tests so that we can check to see if the cancer cells have changed, perhaps morphing into another type, which might impact our treatment plan.

I am still in this fight. I guess sometimes I forget that this enemy doesn't take a vacation. This means I can't be lulled into submission. I was just thinking about how it's kind of like calling an "audible" in a football game. Since it's Super Bowl weekend, this notion is timely.

Years ago, I read a book by Ken Blanchard and Don Shula (one of my all-time favorite coaches and people) entitled Everyone's a Coach: Five Business Secrets for High-Performance Coaching. *It compares the game of football to business. You come up with a game plan and implement it, but sometimes when you get to the line of scrimmage, you have to call an audible because things aren't setting up as you planned or expected and you need to change things up.*

Well, that's what we'll be doing ... Calling an audible, gathering the info we need to be able to modify our game plan and take control of this game.

Trying to stay pumped up and find the perfect battle cry, I think of one of the phrases coined during one of the Apollo missions, "Failure is not an option." I think I'm *going to take that motto on, or maybe I'll adopt a modi-fied phrase from John Paul Jones: "We have just begun to fight." Or, in keeping with the spirit of Super Bowl week, maybe I'll remember the words of the infamous football coach Vince Lombardi: "We would accomplish many more things if we did not think of them as impossible."*

So, as Vince stated so many years ago, I will not consider beating this cancer an impossible feat. In fact, all I really need to remember are words shared in one of the most important books to guide anyone's life: "I can do all things through Christ who strengthens me" (Philippians 4:13).

February 15, 2013

Whew, it's been a wild ride the last few weeks, and the ride will get a little crazier in the next few weeks. A little travel, a little medical, a little work (kind of), and a whole lot of gratefulness!

The time away in Miami was good. And needed. It allowed me to focus on something other than all this medical junk. As I wrote before, the biopsy came back and yes, it's cancer, which wasn't really a big surprise, but what we found out after that was a surprise.

I've been receiving targeted treatment for a certain type of breast cancer, HER2+. The results of the most recent biopsy show that the cancer is triple negative. What I think that means is that the cancer has morphed and changed characteristics, that I might have a little bit of both cancers running through this body, and that I'll be adding to my treatment plan to attack the triple negative.

In addition to the new biopsy results, my scans came back showing that I've had some growth of nodules in my lungs as well as a few that have shown some shrinkage.

While all this news could be frightening, I'm looking at it as a new opportunity on the attack front. Since we've shown some success in some of the cancer areas such as the bones, clavicle, etc., and some progression in other areas, including the lungs and primary site, possibly the treatment we've been using has helped the areas that HER2 responds to. The progression might be this new triple negative stuff that we haven't been treating at all! So if we bring on a new cocktail and add it to the old standard, we could possibly have success in beating this stuff back. Or, I might turn green and grow six eyes and have a chance to make some money in a sideshow.

Confusing, yes, but we are going to attack it head-on. I met with my doctor and talked about our plan. On my own, I've spoken with Cancer Treatment Centers of America and will be heading to Tulsa on Monday to get a second opinion. My doctor supports this. In addition, I'll be heading to San Antonio the following week to visit the START Center, which is doing some fabulous work in developing anticancer drugs that will improve the quality of life and survival for patients with cancer. I've heard them mentioned several times in the last year by doctors and professionals who are in the forefront of this fight, and I'm excited to be able to get in. From what I can tell, this is the cutting edge of cancer research and treatment, and I'm going to be smack dab in the middle of it.

So the journey continues. As I've said so many times, I'm grateful to be where I am with all the support

I have. I've been blessed and continue to be blessed by the love and care that surrounds me every day from the doctors, medical staff, and my family and friends. It's immeasurable. And overwhelming. And inspiring. I still have a lot of fight in me, and when I start to feel it waning, I receive a card in the mail, a phone call, or a text message … A sign from God that I am where I am supposed to be, doing what He wants me to do. I believe that God is encouraging me. As it says in 2 Corinthians 1:4, God "… encourages us in our every affliction, so that we may be able to encourage those who are in any affliction with the encouragement with which we ourselves are encouraged by God."

March 2, 2013

March already? Where did February go? The good news is, I'm still around causing trouble (just ask Joe or Tony or Jesse or …). It's been a very busy month, and here's an update on Cindy's Cancer Tour, Part 1.

I spent a week in Oklahoma at the Cancer Treatment Centers of America (CTCA), and Oklahoma really is O.K.! I have never seen such a patient-oriented environment or felt as comfortable in a medical environment as I did there. I had just reached baggage claim at the airport (yes, I did over pack for a four-and-a-half-day stay, but what's new?) when a woman ran up to me and started raving about how well her father was treated at the center and how I was in such good hands. (She was there picking up her luggage and had seen the driver from the treatment center holding his sign.) As I waited for the driver to pull around, her mother came running in and blessed me and my other CTCA cohort; she too was gushing about how wonderful the hospital was. I was looking around for the hidden camera, thinking that surely this was staged. I guess I've been watching too much reality TV.

Not to bore you with the details of the week, but suffice it to say that I was very impressed! I met with a variety of doctors and advisors, not just my oncologist but also a nutritionist, psychologist, naturopathic doctor, internist, radiologist, manicurist, esthetician ... Oh, those last two were just an added bonus to my stay. Let's just say I got a pretty good going-over.

Joe joined me for the final visit with the oncologist where we talked treatment plan. The office was quite full as my lead doctor was joined by another doctor and two nurse representatives who help keep you on track through your treatment. The treatment plan was presented and included a focus on the new type of cancer that has apparently taken form in this old body. Also included was a new treatment still being investigated for approval by the FDA that shows great promise.

Joe and I were so happy to hear that we still have weapons to help us fight this battle, as my Dallas doctor has assured us. We had the chance to meet with the leadership at the center and were very impressed with everyone we spoke with. And the food was great!

Driving home, we did a lot of discussing and decided that our final decision would come after a visit to the START Clinic in San Antonio (Cindy's Cancer Tour, Part 2).

Once we arrived in San Antonio, we picked up Ellen from the airport and were off on our adventure. After some initial blood work, we met with the doctor who explained this new clinical trial. Apparently, they've had some great results from this three-year-old study, not only with breast cancer but with several other types. The drug is being tested in four locations, Boston, UCLA, Carolina (can't remember which one), and San Antonio. My doctor does not have any triple negative patients enrolled yet, but so far the results from the other patients have been very promising with minimal side effects, including some tummy issues and additional trips to the bathroom. Since this is not uncharted territory for me and is easier to manage than the hand and foot syndrome that impacted my walking and the mouth sores that impacted my talking (heaven forbid I can't talk), these side effects sound like a piece of cake.

After consulting with my medical posse — Joe, Ellen, and Jesse — we all feel like the San Antonio option is the best at this time. The doctor assured me I'll be tested after two months to see if the treatment is working. If for some reason I have doubts sooner than this, I can be tested earlier. Since I have discomfort and tenderness in the left breast area, I'm certain I'll be able to judge if we're having success before the scheduled scans. Thus, I'll be going to San Antonio for a week during spring break to become Patient 79.

I am very comfortable and excited to be part of another clinical study. We found out about one week ago that the second drug I was given in one of the previous studies (TDM1) was approved by the FDA and will be used as a standard care of treatment for cancer patients.

It's so gratifying to know that although I have to deal with this crappy disease, I can possibly help women down the road by participating in these studies while receiving cutting-edge treatment myself, so bring it on!

I know there are many people praying for me, and that brings me great comfort. The notes and calls and messages really help. I feel scared and overwhelmed at times, but it seems like whenever I hit one of those dark times, a little sign reminds me that I'm not alone. I am constantly reminded of how important family and friends are when undergoing something like this. I am blessed to be part of an incredible circle that really rallies together when times get tough. I wish everyone were as blessed as I am in that department.

I also find solace in the fact that perhaps this whole adventure is for something greater. As it says in James 1:2–4, "Consider it all joy, my brothers, when you encounter various trials, for you know that the testing of your faith produces perseverance. And let perseverance be perfect, so that you may be perfect and complete, lacking in nothing."

April 9, 2013

As I was sitting with my daily readings this morning, one of the messages that jumped out at me was about principles we should teach our kids. Specifically, it was, "Show them how to adapt to change."

Wow, nothing could be truer. The passage went on to say, "When you get stuck in the past, it's always at the expense of the future. After the initial shock is over and your anger has dissipated, start making plans." (The Word for You Today, Legacy Church, Albuquerque, NM.)

Well, making plans seems to be where I've been these past few days.

The last trips to San Antonio aren't quite the adventure they were initially, and that drive isn't fun. I'm not really feeling any difference in my body, which I thought would miraculously happen after the first dose. In fact, I'm afraid the change might be for the worse rather than the better.

Then I came back home to learn that a true inspiration in the fight for life against metastatic breast cancer, Bridget Spence, has died at age twenty-nine. She was only twenty-one when she was first diagnosed. As I've mentioned before, I've been honored to be part of a roundtable that Susan G. Komen put together to focus on the ugly truths of metastatic breast cancer. The ladies involved received an email from Komen sharing this sad news.

I have to admit, it sent me into a tailspin. It has taken several days for me to shake it off and pull out of my personal pity party. Please read Bridget's story if you haven't already. It really illustrates what the fight against metastatic breast cancer involves. It's an ongoing, lifetime battle, however long or short that might be, against a disease for which there is no cure.

The shock, the sadness, the anger rocked through our group. One of the members of the roundtable expressed her feelings very eloquently, and I'd like to share them with you because she speaks so well for all of us:

We need focused research to change incurable metastatic breast cancer into a treatable, chronic condition like HIV-AIDS — where patients can now live for twenty to thirty years with treatment after their diagnosis.

If homosexual men, who were then scorned by society in the 1980s, could demand and receive focused research and treatments for their disease, why can't we women — who are wives, mothers, daughters, sisters, grandmothers, AND over half of the population — receive similar research that will find strategies to keep us alive for twenty to thirty years? Are we not worthy of this effort? Are we ignored because we quietly live with our disease?

How many more thousands of us must die before the public and our sisters, who have survived early stage breast cancer, stand with us and for us?

I think back to when I first heard that Magic Johnson had HIV. I was sad to think that his life would be cut short. Now here it is, twenty-two years later, and he's still living and thriving. That's all any of us want, the opportunity to adapt to a change in our lives, not a life that is cut short.

Something that has helped me stay focused on the good that can come from bad situations is a book I just finished reading by my friend Steve Peifer, A Dream So Big: Our Unlikely Journey to End the Tears of Hunger.

Steve and his wonderful wife, Nancy, and their two sons moved to Kenya in the late '90s after losing their youngest son at eight days old. They initially went for a year to work as dorm parents, and continue to live there today, changing thousands of lives through their work, love, and faith. A Dream So Big is the incredible story of how they rallied through their grief to do remarkable things, living a lifestyle that many of us would not want to experience for even a day.

Steve is the most humble and selfless man I have ever met, and handsome too (I add that because I know he will read this). He has coordinated prayers for me in Kenya, and for that I am truly grateful. When you read his story, you will realize how completely humbling it is to know that people across the world, living such simple lives where water and just one pair of shoes are a luxury, even care what is happening to an old lady in a place where a big concern is what type of mobile phone we're going to get (or get for our kids). It makes me pause and remember how truly blessed I am to live in a place where I have doctors and medical care available to give me extra days, months, years.

As I get over the initial shock of the news of Bridget's death and my anger at losing someone so young to this disease begins to subside, I will pay attention to the closing words of my reading that says, "Draw closer to God and decide to live again. Don't get stuck in a stage that was just meant to be part of a process. This too shall pass; let it!"

Although we shouldn't forget Bridget or all the others who have lost their lives to this disease and those who are still fighting it, let's use our anger, sadness, and shock to fuel our efforts to make it better for those still here. Steve Peifer is doing this. He knows all about fulfilling the purpose the Father has for him.

"'For I know the plans I have for you,' declares the Lord, 'plans to prosper you and not to harm you, plans to give you hope and a future'" (Jeremiah 29:11).

April 21, 2013

I keep remembering the first words I heard from one of my doctors at MD Anderson: "This will not be a sprint; it will be a marathon." Little did I realize how true those words would be.

As I feared, my scan results from San Antonio show that the cancer involving the chest wall has grown, as have the spots in my lungs. After speaking with the doctor last Monday, I stopped the clinical trial and have arranged to fly out to the Cancer Treatment Centers of America in Tulsa. I will be leaving Wednesday morning and staying at least one night, maybe two, so we can start a new treatment. No more clinical trials for a while; we'll be looking at a standardized treatment that has shown results for other patients in the past.

We have to get the tumor growth under control, and tomorrow would not be soon enough for me. I can definitely feel the growth involving the chest wall, and that makes it a little more difficult psychologically. Up until the last couple of days, good old Aleve has been enough to keep some of the discomfort in check, but I've had to resort to a little stronger painkiller a couple of times. If I seem a bit lightheaded at times, I'm going to blame it on the drug. That's my story, and I'm sticking to it!

My heart goes out to all those who have been affected by the bombings and the explosion just south of us in Waco, Texas. It reminds me how quickly things can change for each of us and how grateful we must be for each day we are given. It also reminds me of the greater love that surrounds each of us if we will take the time to see it. There truly is something greater than each of us, and for that I am thankful!

I am also thankful I'm still in this race. I think of the pictures we saw of those who were finishing up the Boston Marathon and, in spite of their fatigue, turned back to help those who were impacted by the blast. I hope I can be as strong. Although hobbled and tired, I am still moving forward.

"God is our refuge and our strength, an ever-present help in distress" (Psalm 46:2).

May 18, 2013

So here's the update. I am in the process of daily radiations here in Dallas for six weeks, Monday through Friday. We are targeting the tumor that has sprung up on the sternum and is causing quite a bit of discomfort. I just finished the first week and have five more to go. The discomfort has subsided a bit. Not sure if that's a direct result of the radiation or this pain patch I'm wearing.

My trip to Oklahoma last week brought about a new treatment plan, and I won't be returning again until the radiation is done, in five weeks or more. In the meantime, I'll be doing weekly blood tests to make sure the counts are on track along with the daily zap of radiation. As anything new presents itself, we'll deal with it on a day-by-day basis. We are still speaking with doctors to make sure we're on track to beat this thing the best way we can.

This disease really, really stinks. While you hate to focus on it, there are constant reminders that it's a daily battle. Just when you feel like you're making progress and there's a good end in sight, you're jarred by the news that someone you love, or someone close to someone you love, has been struck. Or you read in the headlines that a celebrity has made a decision to be proactive in heading off the disease.

Hopefully, all the attention will bring progress in changing the outcomes for so many people stricken by cancer. You have to wonder, when you hear about all the money going to impact this disease, what's taking so long?

I continue to plug away, doing what I can to make some type of impact while I'm here. I'm a much bigger crybaby these days and can shed a tear at the drop of a hat. Not that I'm sad all the time, but I truly, truly, truly am overwhelmed by the outpouring of love and support from so many special people in my life, some of whom I have not even met.

I'm grateful that it's a beautiful Saturday morning, I feel like the fog has finally lifted, and I'm feeling somewhat human again. Many times people say that they feel blessed, and you wonder what they mean. I am sure there are many levels of feeling blessed, but I have to share that I've never experienced the feelings of being blessed as I have these last few weeks. Now that the fog has finally lifted, I might say that I am beyond blessed; I am blessed!

Through it all, my incredible support team has been here, starting with Joe, who in spite of working hard to provide for this family, has hovered over me, doing whatever he can to entice me to eat, make me comfortable, and keep my spirits up. The jokes aren't always funny, but God knows he tries to keep things light. Jesse and Tony have been awesome as well, helping to pick up the slack where they can. I sometimes feel guilty that they have to mess with this type of stuff, but I expect this experience will give them life lessons that will help them as they deal with the curveballs life throws at them in the future. I like to think I'm shaping them to be incredible husbands of the future. They only have to look to Joe to find a great role model.

And then there are my incredible sisters and their families, whether God-given or acquired, accompanying me on my trips for treatment, encouraging me along the way, or just sitting in silence when quiet is all that can be managed. It is truly a gift to have people in your life who can just sit and be with you, who don't feel the need *to fill the silence with chatter or noise, who know that their mere presence gives you the comfort and support you need at that moment. In this crazy busy world we live in, how many of us are lucky enough to have people in our lives who are willing to sit and do nothing for hours on end but act like amoebas? Or talk about gross bodily stuff? Or, even worse, watch gross bodily stuff happen? So yes, I am <u>blessed</u>!*

Heck, on Mother's Day, a highlight was having all my boys sprawled in my room, one napping in bed next to me, one napping on the floor, and one busy making a homemade card expressing his love! (You can figure out who was who.) It could have been one of those MasterCard commercials; it was priceless! Not the original plan but an unexpected good moment.

The cards, gifts, and expressions of love catch me off guard at times, and there is no way I can ever return all the loving gestures that have been shared. What I can do is continue to fight to make a difference in the war on cancer, share the lessons I've learned so that somewhere along the way, someone else might benefit, and remind you that the greatest gift of all is love.

"Love is patient, love is kind. It does not envy, it does not boast, it is not proud. It is not rude, it is not self-seeking, it is not easily angered, it keeps no record of wrongs. Love does not delight in evil but rejoices with the truth. It always protects, always trusts, always hopes, always perseveres. Love never fails ... And now these three remain: faith, hope and love. But the greatest of these is love" (1 Corinthians 13:4–8, 13).

Now go and curl up in bed with someone you love or spend some moments in silence offering your gift of love!

In spite of Cindy's continued grace and courage, Joe had the overwhelming feeling they were losing ground. Cindy wasn't responding to treatment, and she was slowly losing her energy and strength. The area on her sternum that was causing a great deal of discomfort required radiation treatments, and that forced her to be off the chemo. Meanwhile, her shortness of breath suggested the cancer was progressing in her lungs. When they went to see their family doctor, Joe's heart nearly stopped when he heard the term "palliative care." These words didn't indicate a plan for recovery; they meant the focus was on keeping Cindy comfortable in the limited time she probably had left.

Nonetheless, Cindy remained positive and continued to love her family and friends with every ounce of strength she had.

June 10, 2013

I definitely am feeling better than I was several weeks ago. My mind is clearer, there's no nausea to speak of, and I'm eating again. Our goal now is for me to put on the weight that I lost, and Joe is doing his best to help me reach my goal. Ice cream, nuts, guacamole, cheese. The challenge is to eat foods that will help you gain weight but are still good for you. When you read all the articles about the good foods for fighting cancer, they often don't correlate to foods that help you pack on the pounds. So that is my quandary.

I'm trying to keep up with my walking, and although I'm taking shorter walks, I still enjoy getting out when I can with my BFF for our morning therapy. If Barbara isn't available, I substitute my dog, Maggie, for a couple trips around the block. The only problem is that Maggie makes me stop so that she can sniff a lot more than Barbara does. Barbara only stops when she spots a lucky penny in the street.

The walks are definitely a highlight of my day! I am planning to participate in the three-day walk again this year at some level, and I know the team has been busy training, so I have to stay in shape. I may not get in sixty miles, but I'll get something in. We have a great team of CC's Sisters pulling together to make a difference.

Trips to Tulsa are on hold for a while as Joe and I visit other doctors. We have visited with my original oncologist and have a visit planned for tomorrow with another. We just want to make sure we're doing everything possible in this fight. Our visit last week reinforced the message that we still have options. We discussed several treatments that have shown promising results as well as another center that specializes in clinical trials. Discussion turned to vaccines, which have also shown promise.

As you know, I was involved with a trial vaccine last year and seemed to have good results, although we couldn't prove they were due to the vaccine. Because of the testing conditions and the fact that no results had been published in years, we decided to stop. We discussed this with our oncologist, who gave this decision her blessing. Although there is research on vaccines, this facility hadn't published any results on controlled studies in years. She (our oncologist) didn't want to discourage us from trying other treatments in conjunction with the chemo, but she didn't have a lot of confidence in the efficacy of the vaccine.

Joe and I would happily empty the bank for a proven treatment plan ... Sadly, this option didn't qualify, but now there's a chance I might have access to a vaccine in a managed environment with reduced personal expense. The key to this process is having options.

Remember, "No trial has come to you but what is human. God is faithful and will not let you be tried beyond your strength; but with the trial he will also provide a way out, so that you may be able to bear it" (1 Corinthians 10:13).

July 7, 2013

Well, as I continue to swim, the tide continues to shift.

I'm happy to say I've been done with radiation for almost three weeks, thank you God. Although my previous experiences with radiation have not been bad, this one wasn't quite as easy. Because the radiation stream was more at the surface, and because I have not been blessed with thick skin, my skin burned quite a bit. I stayed close to home in loose t-shirts so the area could heal more quickly and focused on keeping it lubed up with a salve.

To follow up the fun of radiation, I decided to celebrate with scans so we could get this show on the road and then went back to see the doctor who has treated me for two years. The scans didn't give us the news we were looking for, but at least we have more information to work with. The scans showed some very small areas of concern in the liver and other areas that we'll be watching, but nothing too major. The lungs and chest area are a different story, one that I sense will be more troubling. There is definitely progression in the lungs with some pretty good growth in a couple of the tumors.

The reason I sense something troubling is that I feel an impact on my breathing and am experiencing shortness of breath. I've had to cut back on my walking (which I hate, and Maggie hates even more). My appetite is nil and my energy level is reduced. If I sound like a big ol' weenie, I kind of have been. I am so thankful for my boys who have been waiting on me hand and foot and for my friends who have pitched in as well.

During these last few weeks, although slowed down quite a bit, I was still able to attend the National Komen

Leadership Conference in Dallas. I got the chance to share my story with corporate partners and affiliates as well as to sit on a panel with Dr. George Sledge, who is now chief of oncology at Stanford School of Medicine and a chief scientific advisor for Komen. I remain so appreciative of all the work Komen does to help women and families impacted by breast cancer and more so by the research it funds. Hearing people like Dr. Sledge speak, a doctor who is down in the trenches every day, treating women who are holding on to hope, while he continues to work to find what that hope will look like, makes me determined to stay in this fight.

So tomorrow we start a new chemo plan, a new mixture that will target the cancer this tricky disease has morphed into, and push ahead to shrink the tumors that will help my breathing. When my conversational abilities are impacted, you know we're talking serious business and that I can't waste any time in getting my conversational flow back. I have so much to say!

Right now the plan is an infusion once a week for two weeks, with one week off. The side effects are supposed to be much easier than the killer treatment that knocked me out before. Yeah!

Now an apology to you. I find I have gotten very bad at answering and returning phone calls and sometimes emails, so bear with me. I am pretty good at texting (although maybe not promptly) but sometimes have to pause a little bit before I take action. Sometimes it's energy level; sometimes it's more mindset. If you have a special occasion that I usually remember, please know I probably remembered the date because of my trusty, handy dandy calendar, offered up a quiet prayer of love and good wishes, and can't wait to hear how you celebrated.

As much as people complain about Facebook, for me it has become a connection that allows me to keep up with family and friends (no, not stalking) and get my voice out there when I can't fight that urge. I love seeing all the holiday pics, the celebrations, hearing good news, experiencing a concert — you name it. I love those silly cat/ dog pics, the baby photos, the inspirational thoughts, the lame jokes, getting updates on the latest scientific discoveries, and more. I am doing a lot of surfing, all for a good reason, and I'm staying dry.

The plan is that tomorrow is a new day, I'm going to spend some special time with my boys and celebrate Jesse's twenty-seventh birthday, and then come back at this stuff stronger than ever.

"Not only so, but we also glory in our sufferings, because we know that suffering produces perseverance; perseverance, character; and character, hope. And hope does not put us to shame, because God's love has been poured out into our hearts through the Holy Spirit who has been given to us" (Romans 5:3–5).

This was Cindy's next to last journal entry and her final trial, as she would lose her battle with metastatic breast cancer just seven weeks later. She continued to have a positive outlook, believing the issue with her lungs was just a tumor that could be shrunk with the right drugs, but the truth was that her lungs were damaged, the damage was accelerating, and treatment options were becoming less and less viable.

Since both Cindy and Joe had grown up on the East Coast (Miami for her, outside of New York City for him) and they both loved salt water, waves, and gulls, Joe set up a quick trip to South Padre Island with the boys, thinking it would give Cindy a psychological boost.

Almost immediately, he began questioning the decision to make this trip. Cindy's health had significantly diminished, and her appetite was completely gone. She could not find a comfortable position in the car, even though she was sitting on soft heated leather, with extra pillows. Once they arrived, she was too weak to go down to the beach. Instead, she sat on the balcony for a little while, then retreated to the bedroom with an encompassing view of the beach, where she stayed for three days.

Joe felt helpless. Though many women had recovered from breast cancer, it was becoming all too clear that Cindy wasn't going to be one of them.

A few days after they returned from South Padre Island, Joe took Cindy for an x-ray because the doctor wanted to see what was going on in her lungs before starting the next round of chemo. When the doctor saw the mass, she consulted with the pulmonologist in the hopes of drawing out what she thought was fluid build-up. Instead, the specialist told her what she was seeing could not be withdrawn because it wasn't fluid build-up; it was the cancer advancing.

In the hallway, Joe and the doctor had a conversation that confirmed Joe's worst fears. He'd known in his heart this was coming, but he simply wasn't prepared to hear it.

He recalled, "It took all my energy to go back into the room with Cindy and keep my composure. We sat together for a little while, letting it slowly sink in. We were losing; we just didn't yet know how little time we had left." He added, "We didn't know what to do, what to say, or who to call. How did we even share this kind of news?"

One week later, in another private conversation, the doctor estimated that Cindy had only a couple of weeks left.

As the words sank in, complete shock and disbelief overcame Ellen, who along with their sister Debbie had accompanied Cindy to this appointment. Ellen asked if the doctor meant two weeks, and the answer was yes. All Ellen could think was, "How do we walk back in that room and act normally? How do we put on a brave face and tell her what we must?"

It was incredibly difficult to hear this news, but the two sisters drew on their faith and Cindy's continued strength and courage in the face of insurmountable odds. Essentially, they boxed up their emotions and relied on each other to make it through what was next.

Somehow, in the precious here and now, Cindy continued to inspire those around her, as the following chapter relays.

Chapter Four
THE COLANGELO KIBBUTZ

"I want to have all the people I love together at one big party."

— Cindy Colangelo

Cindy's family and friends watched her fight the battle of her life (and for her life) for more than four years in what they called "the arena." They saw her stumble and get back up. They rallied with her every setback and watched her maintain her enthusiasm and dignity. They saw the gracious way she faced each and every challenge, including her dismay at the polarizing and destructive battle between Planned Parenthood and Komen, the very organization that raises hundreds of millions of dollars specifically for breast cancer research.

When the doctors had exhausted all their treatments, Cindy's family was tasked with telling her the news. There was no easy way to approach the delivery of such crushing news, so Joe, Ellen, Jesse, Deb, and Anne postponed the inevitable until the following day and drowned their sorrows in a good bottle of tequila that evening instead.

When they delivered the news the next day, Cindy was unbelievably calm, and the situation felt very surreal. Ellen recalled, "We asked her, 'What do you want to do? You only have so much time left. We will do anything you want; just tell us.'"

Cindy decided that she wanted a party. She wanted to see all the people she cared about and loved together at one big party, which she was always partial to.

So, Ellen, Joe, Jesse, and Tony led the charge. Cindy decided on a Tuesday that she wanted the party and then insisted that it be held that Friday, a mere three days later.

"We tried to tell her that people were working on Friday and that it was only a couple of days away," Joe said. "She said, 'No, I don't know how I'm going to feel on Saturday.' She said it matter-of- factly. It was like she knew that one day could make all the difference. She said, 'I want it Friday. Saturday will be too late.'"

So Friday it was. In three short days, Cindy's family and friends threw together the party of a lifetime. In true Cindy style, she gave the family her marching orders. She provided a guest list, and her family made phone calls and spread the word via Facebook and texting, enlisting friends to do the same.

The day of the party was madness. Joe, Ellen, Jesse, and others drove to the airport and grocery store multiple times, all the while making and answering phone calls and caring for Cindy.

Ellen said, "I think we were all on a major adrenaline rush. We weren't sure what to expect, and we were all still trying to grasp the reality of what was happening around us and to our Cindy. The thought that this was her final party was very hard to grasp."

The weather that day was incredibly hot, and the family rearranged the furniture throughout the house to make Cindy comfortable and accommodate a crowd. Meanwhile, family and friends from all over the country pitched in with food and drinks.

"We had no expectations on how the party would play out," Ellen said. "We just invited everyone Cindy instructed us to invite and waited to see what would happen."

What happened was astonishing. Hundreds of people from across the country showed up at the Colangelo household to see Cindy. They came from Baltimore, Miami, Georgia, and all over Texas. Those who could not attend in person threw parties at their own homes, sending photos and notes of love, showing Cindy they wanted to be in the final arena with her.

All of Cindy's siblings and numerous cousins came, not to mention friends from high school and college, some of whom the Colangelos hadn't seen in years. In fact, people came from every phase of Cindy's life, lining the neighborhood streets with cars, and forming a line out the front door.

The kitchen and dining room tables and all the countertops were filled with food, but it was so crowded that no one could get to it. It was over one hundred degrees that day, not unusual for August in Texas, but with so many people coming and going, the air conditioners could not keep up. Joe rented several "swamp coolers" for the outdoors in an attempt to regulate the temperature, and people stood in the front and back yards, the garage, even the alley. The neighbors let the family borrow their garbage and recycling bins, and these stayed full for weeks.

"Cindy was thrilled!" Ellen recalled. "Although she was beyond exhausted and needed many breaks, she wanted to see everybody. That's where she drew her strength. She was able to experience the love she'd been receiving near and far for the past few years from all these people at the same time in one room."

While Joe, Tony, and Jesse welcomed everyone, Ellen served as "gatekeeper" to prevent Cindy, whose energy was waning, from being overwhelmed. Because she didn't have the energy to talk to everybody, they pushed her swivel rocker into the corner of the living room where she could view everyone. Friends formed a line, and everybody spent their couple of minutes with her.

Many friends and family members stayed for several days, and some stayed longer, including Cindy's oldest sister, Anne, and her friend Amy. In fact, as many as twelve additional people stayed with the family in the weeks following the party; air mattresses were scattered throughout the house. Joe said it in jest, but thus was born "the Colangelo Kibbutz."

During this extended family time, Cindy outlined to each of these special people how she wanted them to live the rest of their lives. Joe ruefully admits, "Her admonishment to her niece about 'no more tattoos' was broken soon afterwards." He adds, "It really was a blessing that she spent her last few weeks with her closest friends and family all around her."

As was typical of Cindy, she defiantly lived longer than the doctors predicted. Her final journal entry, which appears below, was written in late August, a few days before she passed away; Ellen posted it on September 2.

Cindy was too weak to write, so she dictated what she wanted to say to Joe and to her childhood best friend and college roommate, Amy. Those who knew Cindy knew she often got lost telling a joke, which usually became just as funny as the joke itself. True to form, Joe and Amy had to patiently work with her to get the wishing well story, dictated below, just right.

September 2, 2013

It's time for my final CaringBridge journal entry. I've been given the gift of sharing my story with you, the tough times and the good, and all the love that has surrounded me throughout this experience. It has been a glorious ride, not always pretty, but one that seems to leave a lesson in its path. Each person has played a part, some for a short while, some for a lifetime, but each equally valuable.

When I was younger, a priest told a story of a little boy and the wishing well. Every day, the boy would run up to it and yell, "I hate you!" and what would come back was "I hate you!"

For days and days, he would yell, "I hate you!"

This evolved into weeks and months. The response always came back, "I hate you!"

One day, a robin at the corner of the well suggested the little boy yell, "I love you!"

The little boy tried it, and a voice yelled back "I love you!"

Again, the little boy yelled, "I love you!" and again, "I love you!" was the response.

I've learned through all my experiences that we should be sending out messages of love in order to get love in return.

All my love and blessings. I'll be watching you.

Cindy Lou

Epilogue

CINDY LOU, FROM BEGINNING TO END

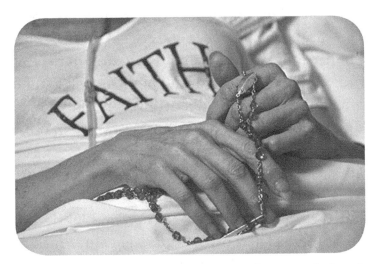

"I got my strength from her — a candy-coated chunk of granite."

—Joe Colangelo

In the end, Joe, Ellen, Jesse, Tony, Anne, and Amy were with Cindy when she left on her final journey.

Her passing was peaceful; she just slowly drifted away. In spite of their terrible grief, everyone present felt a sense of closure and peace. Cindy's final days were an incredible testimony to a beautiful life, and her faith was never stronger. She even embraced the hospice caregivers who surrounded her, wanting to know their names, hear their stories, and understand their lives.

In many respects, Cindy went out on her own terms. She made good use of her remaining time with those she loved, and she left a permanent mark on those she came in contact with, most especially her two beloved sons, in whom she leaves a lasting legacy.

The last days and weeks of her life were spent in hospice care at her home. Cindy went from spending most of her time in a chair in the living room to lying in her bed. Eventually, she had to move to a hospital bed. She was none too happy about this, since it meant she couldn't sleep with Joe, but it was necessary in order to give her the care she needed.

In her final days, even though her communication was limited to an occasional eye blink, her family continued to read to her, talk to her, and let her know who was there. The hospice nurse gave her massages, and Amy rubbed Cindy's feet. They played her favorite Christian music, read her favorite Bible verses, and took turns assisting the nurses throughout the days and nights.

On Cindy's final day, the family felt an overwhelming urge to leave the house and have dinner together. Tony had started his first days of high school, and they knew Cindy was comforted by that fact. Everything was taken care of, and it was perhaps the perfect time to slip away, knowing that all the people she cared about would be okay.

After being encouraged by the nurses to leave the house, something they had not done together since they were told of Cindy's fate six weeks prior, the group went to a favorite family restaurant, all the while expecting a text requesting them to return home. Upon their return, they were welcomed by a nurse named Destiny, with whom Cindy had formed a close bond.

The minute they returned to the house, the family felt a change in the air. They walked into Cindy's room, sensing that her time was limited. Ellen pulled out her Bible and started to read Cindy's favorite passages. Tears streaming from their eyes, holding hands, they laid a rosary in Cindy's hand and prayed. As Psalm 23 from the prayer card of Cindy's mother-in-law was being read, Cindy slowly slipped away. Her last breath was peaceful; she was surrounded by her family and their love.

Ellen recalls, "We were sad but joyful as she finally reached the end of her journey. Her long battle was over, but she had not lost. It was the kind of experience you read about."

Cindy's father's health had been in decline, but he and Cindy's mom had made the trip to Dallas to spend their daughter's last days with her. A few weeks after Cindy's death, he, too, entered hospice care and died shortly thereafter. It was a dream of Cindy's to write a book with her father about his family's old-fashioned drug store in Miami, and it is now Ellen's and her sisters' hope to fulfill this dream for Cindy.

In the meantime, Joe and the rest of Cindy's family hope that others will draw strength from Cindy and the legacy she leaves behind in *Candy-Coated Chunk of Granite*. Her desire to help others facing significant life challenges and braving uncertain futures pulled her through her own tough times. In turn, time and time again, she exemplified the art of living courageously and showed the importance of giving back while loving and living fully until the final day.

Cindy documented her struggle for four years and five months. During that time, she sought answers. She sought solace. She sought a cure. While she did not find this cure, she did find a powerful answer to the question everyone asks sooner or later: What is the meaning of life?

Her meaning was found in her family, her friends, and her faith. In other words, in love. As Jesse commented, "My mom always saw the good in people and never met a person she didn't like. It's a lesson I try to keep with me at all times."

We hope you find the same inspiration here.

The final note (below) on the CaringBridge website was posted by Joe in his first public step without Cindy.

September 7, 2013

I'd like to express my gratitude to all those who have shared kind words or helped in some way during the final two months of Cindy's battle. More than a few family members and friends from out of town stayed at "the Colangelo Kibbutz" to be with her and comfort her.

Cindy fought with an amazing determination and positive attitude and did not wilt under the emotional and physical stress of stage IV cancer. She would occasionally refer to me as her rock, but I got my strength from her — a candy-coated chunk of granite.

This miserable disease created the opportunity for Cindy to touch many lives and initiate a deeper spiritual growth. In the end, cancer took her body, but her soul had been placed out of reach and is now in eternal peace with the Lord. For this, and for the gifts she shared while she was with us, we celebrate.